Meet the Ladies -

*- In this light-hearted guide on how to survive
the battle of the sexes.
Twenty-one unforgettable women reveal all!!*

*A collection of short pieces originally written
for the stage
Hilarious, moving and inspiring
In their own words, the stories of Dulcie,
matriarch of the British Raj –
Venus the Love Goddess –
Ivy and the denizens of Fagg Street (including
the outrageous Roxie) -
Marilyn the pantomime Fairy -
Belma, who 'Almost Knew Ivor Novello' -
And many more.*

Lavishly illustrated with rare theatrical postcards
featuring stars of the early 20th century,
this is a delightful companion for any spare moment.

**For all men who ever tried to get along with women!
And all women who can't understand why they don't!**

Miss Zena and Miss Phyllis Dare

Living with Women

*A Survivor's Guide
On and Off the Stage*

by
Paul Gater

Anecdotes Publishing

ISBN: 9781898670 124
Text copyright © Paul Gater 2008

British Library Cataloguing in Publication Data:
A catalogue record for this book
is available from the British Library.

Published by: Anecdotes
70 The Punch Bowl, Manchester Road,
Buxton, Derbyshire SK17 6TA

Printed and bound by:
RPM Print & Design, 2-3 Spur Road,
Quarry Lane, Chichester PO19 8PR

The pieces included in Living With Women
may be read or performed in public without fee,
provided the author's name appears on publicity material.
For further information go to
www.anecdotespublishing.co.uk

To Graham
a true showman
and a true friend
with many thanks
for your support and
encouragement

CONTENTS
Introduction by Alicia Crow

A Short History of Theatrical Postcards
The Stars – An Alphabetical Index
By Alicia Crow

Friday, April 12, 1957. Graham F. Humphreys is pictured with up-and-coming stars Dilys Laye and Donald Sinden at the Press Showing of Doctor at Large at the Astoria, Charing Cross Road. His then girlfriend Maura Bowes, a dancer with the Television Toppers on the Billy Cotton Band Show, is on the right.

Graham Humphreys was trained at the Rank School of Theatre Management, based at the Gaumont Theatre, Finchley, London. His training included a spell at Pinewood Studios and he worked with many well-known British film and stage personalities from the 1950s onwards. He also worked as House Manager at the ICA.
Now retired, he devotes his time to his extensive collection of film and theatre memorabilia.

Foreword
by
Graham F. Humphreys
F.I.E.M, A.F.C.I.

Member: The Managers' Round Table
of the Motion Picture Herald

In nearly 50 years as a theatre and cinema manager, I have been privileged to spend my working life in the company of many lovely ladies – whether in person or on film. I met 'starlets' of the Rank Charm School like Magda Miller and Shirley Eaton, as well as established British stars such as Ursula Howells and Helen Cherry; I managed stage shows for such performers as Winifred Atwell, Dorothy Squires and Lita Roza; while on screen, I have shown the films of all the major Hollywood and world stars.

I am not ashamed to reveal that I have always loved the ladies! – though my personal favourite beauties changed all the time, because of the many lovely women I encountered, whether 'in the flesh' or on-screen. My working life was carried out in an atmosphere of 'top hat, white tie and tails' – not quite, though in my day, the Theatre Manager always wore bow tie and dress suit. Going to the theatre was an occasion, the very epitome of glamour.

Those glamorous years of the 20th century will never be seen again, and in my opinion, they will never be equalled. I find the wonderful elegance and sophistication of the 30s and 40s a constant inspiration, though the Edwardian era was also, as the pictures in this book show, the epitome of glamour.

I can personally vouch for this, since both my grandfather and my father were master-butchers in the Edgware Road, with a vast number of theatricals among their regular clientele. My grandfather's reminiscences included personal recollections of the theatrical world of his era, including musicians, singers and actresses like Phyllis and Zena Dare (pictured at the beginning of this book) and many others who grace these pages.

My father loved the stage so much that he became a semi-professional entertainer with a song-and-dance act – I still possess the silver-topped cane he used on the stage. Coincidentally, he took the stage name Frank Dare as a tribute to the lovely and talented Dare sisters. In my turn, I too was drawn by the 'smell of the greasepaint, the roar of the crowd'. What worked the magic for me was when as a very young child, I was taken to see the legendary partnership of Fred Astaire and Ginger Rogers on the screen. I knew then this was the world for me.

Showmanship, they say, is something that is in your blood – and it is as showman as well as a collector of theatre ephemera that I invite you to join me in enjoying this unusual and very entertaining book. My collection of theatrical postcards, always a joy to me, can now be shared with readers of Paul Gater's witty 'star turns' and appreciated by a wider audience.

In one respect, I have never regarded my life in film and theatre as 'work'. It has been pure pleasure. A show every night! So now once again, allow me to bid you all – patrons old and new – a warm welcome as the overture strikes up, the lights dim and the curtain rises!

INTRODUCTION

The stars of this book are no strangers to the stage. The main body of the text, originally written to offer solo actresses the chance to perform complete scripts especially for women, first appeared in book form as *Singular Women – One Woman Scripts* in 1999.

'This delightful collection of deceptively simple short pieces offers the opportunity to explore text and character with delicacy and precision,' wrote Gwenda Hughes, then Artistic Director of the New Vic Theatre, Newcastle-under-Lyme, in her Foreword. 'I am sure that audiences and performers alike will enjoy the experience.'

And how right she was! Designed to be played with character easily established by the actress's costume, with or without scenery and easily adaptable to any venue, the pieces were all successfully performed during the years that followed. Arabella, Venus, Bessie and the rest all took their bows in the theatre – both with and without scripts – as well as in many other venues including shops, clubs, libraries, marquees, and village halls both as part of larger productions and as entertainments in themselves. They appeared in and out of doors, and also on radio.

'A unique book,' was the verdict of *Amateur Stage*. '…well-written and well-developed monologues, reflecting the varying ages and backgrounds which allow a lot of scope'; while *Speech and Drama* praised the scripts as '…tales of humour and pathos…from Agnes the bag-lady, via ageing country music star Peggy-Lou, to Angela, the wingless angel.'

It is true that the scripts may still be used to bring the fun and involvement of theatrical experience to fresh audiences – they have proven themselves when used for educational purposes in schools and colleges, and are suitable for presentation in hospitals, retirement homes and so on. But they offer far more than that. They draw on the traditional type of music-hall and seaside postcard humour, commenting wittily but without malice on the eternal themes that pervade the lives of all women and the men who have to try to understand them. It is a mark of the author's skill that though the ladies who appear here are very much their own women, the scripts – particularly the more eccentric characters – may be just as successfully portrayed by male actors 'in drag'.

Illustrated as they are here by rare theatrical postcards from the Edwardian and variety era, the early 1900s – 1920s, the stories take on fresh impetus and charm. Not only the theatrical world is captured here – whether of the pantomime fairy, the song-birds (both Wagnerian and Western) and the aspiring ingenue of Ivor Novello's smash musicals of the 1930s and 40s – but the secret lives of all women, their yearning for romance, their pragmatic acceptance of what life actually doles out to them, their hopes, aspirations and dreams. A sharp, but sympathetic observer of the human condition, Paul Gater's early work was described by *The Times* as 'shrewd, yet subtle'.

This collection offers entertainment on many levels. There are depths of insight, hilarious situations, witty one-liners – and women you will never forget. The sumptuous pictures of stars of stage and screen provide a unique background to a refreshing and fascinating book.

Alicia Crow

Miss Gertie Millar

Miss Pauline Chase as Lady Wilhelmina Belturbet
in The Amazons

1 TABITHA JANE
The Lollipop Lady Strikes Back

Me and my brother Joe, we're just the same. We speak the truth. His big mouth got him elected Mayor - mine got me the job of Lollypop Lady. I fit it in with other things to help out, now Herbert's retired. Well, the uniform – you wouldn't be seen dead in it, except for work. But the kids, bless 'em, they always notice the little things, like a new pair of earrings.

'Just you take your time! You've got your rights!' I tell them, even though the traffic's piling up on all sides of me, with all the lot - two fingers, four-letter words – something shocking.

I just give it them back, those men. I always wave the women drivers through, though, and that makes them worse, having to shunt backwards and forwards – with a few wing mirrors getting knocked off in the process, usually.

'Who's the best drivers now?' I say. Talk about Laurel and Hardy – except that nobody thinks it's very funny.

I make the men wait their turn – if it comes – especially the sort that look like boffins – you know, jump-ups and intellectuals. Four-by-Fours and BMWs, mostly. It's them, the quiet ones, that shout the loudest if you understand my meaning. In a silent sort of way.

It's them that make the laws, you see, not your Government. Like, for instance – Tabitha Jane's not a Lollipop Lady any more but a 'Road Safety Officer'. Using

Mr Fred Terry and Miss Julia Neilson

their state-of-the-art spiel, in this state-of-the-art world as we live in. All this political correctness – like Tabitha Jane dursn't wear her Mam's old musquash, or address some poncy shop assistant as a you-know-what. Or think for herself. It's the law.

But they hadn't reckoned on Tabitha Jane's Law, especially of a Monday morning – or any other school morning, come to that. A spade's a spade – I jolly well say what I like. Same as Joe, my brother. I mean, he even lays on the Civic Jag to take me to work and back again, when the weather is inclement. And with Linford in his fancy chauffeur's gear, it's just like in that film *Driving Miss Daisy.* Folk that wave when I float past them think I'm the late Queen Mother.

What you'd call ambitious, is our Joe. He's not married, but he does have a large tabby called Rambo. Since he got to be Mayor, his mates call him Dick Whittington. It must be second sight – 'cos he says he'd stand for Lord Mayor of London if he had the chance. Mind you, he had to think hard for a Mayorial consort. He couldn't ask an old tabby with four legs – so he asked me. Oh, I was chuffed to little mint balls.

But Herbert – that's my husband – oh, he wasn't. He hates publicity. Even our wedding photos, he would only agree to have the negatives printed.

'You've given me one of me dizzy dos, just thinking about it,' was what he said, nearly flaking out – conveniently into the easy chair. 'You do too much as it is,' he says, 'one thing at a time, that's my motto.'

Well, with my job and helping out at the Mother's Union,

and TWG – and collecting for the Campaign for the Individual's Rights – I suppose I do take a lot on. Still, you never know before till after.

Bods wonder what me and Herbert have in common. He's old enough – nearly – to be my father, but he's happy enough with a pipeful of baccy and his pension book – and his DIY. Of course, nothing ever gets finished. But he's that considerate, you wouldn't believe. Always knocks the nails in with a rubber hammer, so's not to bother me.

Tabitha Jane, on the other hand, she seems to bother folk a great deal. Or so says Mr Silver, the Headmaster – er – Head Teacher – using their state-of-the-art terminology, them boffins I'm talking about. Same difference. Who do they think they are?

I never go looking for trouble, but it seems I always find myself on some warpath. Says Mr Silver: 'Traffic jams as far as Vista Bridge, right down to Holly Way, and never when Annie Thomson was Road Safety Officer, or old Teasdale before that.'

Course, there were a lot more children then, with three schools in the area, and if you listen to Mr Silver: 'They always used to cross in their hordes.'

'Ah-ah! One child at a time, Mr Head-whatever – that's my motto,' I tell him. 'They're dealing with Tabitha Jane now. And with Tabitha Jane, it's the right of the individual that comes first – *right?*

Miss Lily Elsie as Alice and Mr Robert Michaels as Freddy Fairfax in The Dollar Princess

Miss Marie Lohr

2 BELMA
I Almost Knew Ivor Novello

Oh yes, Belma Starr has been around not quite for ever, though exactly how long, I shan't say…

But birthday or not, you're quite right, I'm in no party mood - though I was, until you dropped in to see me. We were all of us thoroughly enjoying ourselves – and yes, you *can* create a happy ambiance if you have a carefree attitude, darling, even in a residential home. Journalists! Tactless just is not the word! How old am I, indeed… No, I don't care if it was meant as a joke!

Of *course* it helps to have a sense of humour, especially here at Happy Endings, albeit under more straitened circumstances. 'All of us are getting nowhere fast,' as that new-fangled playwright Samuel Beckett would have us believe.

I'm sorry dear, I didn't mean to be rude. We *artistes* can be a little brusque at times, I'm afraid. A pity you missed the entertainment this afternoon. But I do know how busy you journalists can be….

Alas, the Great Zappo, with his world famous telepathy act, has not been too well just lately, so he's had to stay up in his room. But, with heaving bosom, Carla Delgardo stepped into the breech – our Spanish soprano – to sing the *Habanera* from Bizet's 'Carmen'. At seventy-five, she is still passionate – . Oh, about the bull-fight, and the string of toreadors she has left lying on their backs, in her wake. Her amazing story would read so *terribly* well on your Showbiz page - though not as well as mine, naturally.

Mr Lewis Waller and Miss Evelyn Millard in Othello

And naturally speaking, you see Conrad Huber, plump little man - over by the window – the 'Great Warbler'? I'll swear this afternoon, his bird impressions sounded better through his dentures than when he had his own teeth. He was really enjoying himself, rippling and chirping away, in German of course.

After 'The Bird' so to 'The Bard' and my dear friend Bibby Haynes, with her 'Gems from Shakespeare' - when she could remember her words, that is... No, dear. She's not here at the moment. Taken ill, in the middle of *The primrose path of dalliance*, she was wheeled out rather quickly. An overindulgence of the prawn salad, I think. Something we don't get every day in this establishment. Word-learning was hard for her, even when she was young, I remember. So shy she was, and retiring. I can see her now, standing in the wings, almost gnawing her fingers away. Yet once on stage, she had such complete control. With the strength, and impact of one of her own heroines – Lady Bracknell herself....

Her specialities? Oh, Ophelia, for one. A favourite with all the critics, although I far preferred her Juliet. And they do say her Blanche Dubois in 'Streetcar Named Desire' at the Grand Theatre, Wolverhampton, was far superior to that of Vivien's in the film. Er...? Vivien *Leigh*, dear.

Our highlight this afternoon should have been Arty Sturgess. He was the Ivor Novello look-alike of his day, before look-alikes were invented. Like Ivor, he acted magnificently – but a fine tenor also. He'd once had hopes of an operatic career, but looked too much like a matinee idol. Why, lots and lots thought he was the most handsome man alive. He could do all the big songs, the set pieces. Slim, agile, always charming – until his bowel operation, last year. Very nasty. Followed by a stroke – even nastier. Though typically, the old trouper rose to the challenge.

Well, not quite. But so *lucky* to be alive – he's hunched up in the far corner over there dear, not speaking to anyone. Just sharing some secret with himself...

13

Knowing that he'd been the best? Possibly so, my dear. There always seemed to be flowers... roses... *'Rose of England'*... and lilacs all over the stage... *'We'll Gather Lilacs in the Spring again.'* It's years since my friend Bibby Haynes and I smelt lilacs. There aren't any here in the gardens, at Happy Endings...

In my opinion, the likes of Noel Coward, Gertie Lawrence, and even the amusing Ciceley Courtneidge and myself – we were not singers, you understand. At least, nowhere near the class of Arty Sturgess. But so. It did not matter. We got by. Like working overseas - when you lived on your wits. You just battled on, *anything* to keep the money coming in. Well, not quite. Although, yes – even 'that', if the show folded, and you hadn't got the fare home.

It was odd how Bibby and I, we'd lose touch, maybe for years – although it happens a lot in the profession. Then, like old pennies, we'd roll back into each other's lives.

We met up once in Singapore, where I'd been entertaining the ex-pats. And Bibby was on her way home, after singing to the forces in Korea. How we celebrated, that night. We always had our admirers. Shaking a leg or two in revue, or sharing the bill with wild-eyed fakirs, or one-eyed buglers riding mono-cycles, there was always some stage-door Johnny to shower us nightly with flowers and jewellery, and invitations to lots of weekend house-parties in the country. And the people you met there were such fun.

But my only true spouse *was* the stage, dear. No more so, I realised, than during a down-turn, early in my career when, to make ends meet, I took a job with Timpsons' Shoes. Then I remember Sadie Everill, my beloved agent, ringing me, one

Miss Gertie Millar and Mr Raymond Lauzerte
in The Tango

afternoon, at the shop, at that appropriate moment - the stuff of legends, as they say. Just after the war.

'Auditions. Such-and-such rehearsal-rooms near Waterloo station,' she barked, like a drill-sergeant. 'Touring production of Ivor Novello's *The Dancing Years.*'

'The Prancing Queers', Ivor jokingly called it. This was the first time I met the dashing, *young* Arty Sturgess, cast as Rudi Klebel - *and* Bibby Haynes, of course. Oh, she claimed to know Ivor well, and fancied playing opposite Arty, in the part of Greta. But Piers Farrow, the director, gave me one of the most gruelling auditions I ever experienced. And I could hardly believe my luck, when he said only *I* was the absolute natural for the part.

Performing with Arty proved a *sensation*. Not only for audiences, but for myself also. Such inspiration, he had so much to teach me. Such a *man* – even now, in spite of his disabilities. Bibby was not too happy as my understudy, I recollect, but our friendship had begun. We were so different, it is true. But there were things in common o' plenty...

No, no, no, my dear. We weren't *that* touring company of elaborate sets and sumptuous costumes, with *Ivor* in the lead part. We were sumptuous enough, I suppose, with another friend Ethel Pope-Wallace at the piano, cousins Chuck and Bunty on cello and double-bass, and Flubber Partridge laying it on with the timpani. The challenge of Sunday travel was nothing. Nor sleeping in waiting-rooms, theatrical digs with bed-bugs, or in cold church halls where we performed. Such adventure - sweeping our nightly audiences up into a world of glittering romance and make-believe, my dear.

Especially in that dreadful winter of 1947 – sometimes, with only oil-lamps to hand.

Then, some time later, I suddenly had this marvellous idea for a musical play. I'd always dabbled in a bit of scribbling. But this time, somehow, it was different. I just knew it would give me my big chance. With two names only - Ivor Novello and my own – Belma Starr – in the leading roles. But not *knowing* Ivor did pose problems...

He *had* dropped in just the once, while we were rehearsing *The Dancing Years,* but he'd disappeared again. And if I'd simply posted my idea to him, it might not have been opened. After all, we know how brusque these *artistes* can be don't we, my dear? The only person I really knew who knew Ivor Novello? My friend, Bibby. Though even to this day, I don't know if there were official invitations, or not. It's possible we simply gate-crashed into Redroofs, Ivor's place, near Maidenhead, that night. But everyone who was anyone in the theatre was there. Edward Marsh, the critic, Binkie – Baumont, of course, darling - Terence Rattigan, Noel Coward... I could reel off more names than there are on a war memorial.

So much music and laughing, horse-play in the swimming pool, even at two o'clock in the morning. And right in the middle of it all – 'the man who made the people sing' – Ivor Novello himself.

'Ivor, *darling!* Bibby called, on the strength of three or four double whiskies, 'I'd love you to meet my friend...' - but it made no impression, with Ivor and Noel talking earnestly together at the pool-side, despite her repeated efforts. So she actually thrust her long cigarette-holder straight into the glass of orange juice he was holding (Ivor rarely touched alcohol, you know) and sucked through it, like a straw. Noel had a fit of the giggles – typically – but Ivor just went quite pale and looked *aghast*.

Then Bibby, all her courage gone, staggered into the lilac-bushes, and was very, very ill. I felt my big chance just slipping away. Even my hot black was melting with embarrassment. (That was what we called our mascara in those days, my dear). And face-to-face with Ivor Novello for the only time in my life, I was unable to think of a single *word*.

Aha. They're wheeling her in again. At last. You're looking so much better Bibby, dear... 'Like Lady Bracknell'? Oh, how absolutely right!

He's still hunched up in the corner – dear Arty, sharing that secret with himself... Consoling himself with past triumphs did you say, my dear? Well, I'm not so sure. I think it's something else - so obvious that we don't even need the Great Zappo, with his mental telepathy act, to tell us...

'All of us getting nowhere fast'? Sorry, dear... It's simply that the show always goes on. And here at Happy Endings, we are *all* old troupers, you know. As for Ivor, well, he never even *saw* old bones, did he?

Miss Billie Burke

3 AGNES
Keep On Dancing

'Sleep for sense, wake up as big a fool as ever'. Hey, what, I must 'a dozed off. It's the air here in the park. Fresh isn't the word. Who's this? Young mum – yer wanting somewhere to sit?

Room here for your little un, love, if I shove up…Oh, all right – bloomin' well be like that!

Well, here's a more familiar face! See you've come up the High Street. Chance you didn't see Mel, did yer? Little fella – with a shopping-bag as old as he is? Councillor Mel Parker – face like a yard o' tripe? I must have missed him today, with dozing off like that. Always stops and has a word, he does. Out shopping most days. For him and his missus, and calling into Doctor Forster's for her prescription once a week.

Her being Fenella – tall, ex-Bluebell Girl. Dancer. Dancer? Couple o' leg thrusts and a shuffle. Rent-a-wreck, with more edge on her than a broken chamber pot. And proud? You can't touch her.

Just like *him* – like my Billy. Master Craftsman, that was him. Cobbler. Made these boots, he did. Real leather, see? He were ever so good to me. Them and a thick coat, they get me through the winter, any road. Now and then, they let wet in. So I mends 'em. Couple of old tyres. Off the rubbish heap. Couple of old inner tubes, you've got yourself a pair o'stockings and all. Blow 'em up, or let 'em down, according to size.

20

Miss Ellen Terry

Hm – used to think he was *one o' them*. One o' them for putting me and my like in the workhouse. Councillor Mel Parker, I'm on about. Little man with busy days. A friendly passer-by. But I was wrong about him, see. Least, I think I was. Despite a certain cock-up.

I blame that Doctor Forster – youngish, *wears an ear-ring.* Not that that should have anything to do with it, mind.

Mr Matheson Lang

'Headaches,' Mel mentioned to him, 'have you got anything for my headaches?' To which Doctor Forster said: 'I want to see your groin.'

'Ooh, that makes yer think!' I said to Mel when he told me.

'An' I'd only gone to collect a prescription for my missus's tablets,' he explained.

'Well! Doctor Forster?' I said. 'And all them young women they say he keeps warm? I should watch him! *Here* – did he have that saucy look in his eye this morning?' But Mel, he wasn't having any o' that. Quick as a flash he came back – 'Not when he looked at my groin, he didn't.'

I first saw Mel years back. In the Public Library. Government Publications Section. White Papers – Urban Environment. Nice, warm in there, it is. An' specially of a winter. 'Doing research,' he said. *Got brains, yer see.* Got hidden depths. Like my Billy.

Course, doctors, they couldn't do a thing for *'im*. Or wouldn't. Always mouthing off. Always knew better, didn't he? But – he were ever so good to me.

Just a small council place we had, him and me. A dump, you'd 'a said. But I saw it as a – sort of love-nest. Top o' Sycamore Street. Best if we'd had a wall knocked down inside, though. Make it bigger.

'Just leave it all to me!' says Councillor Mel Parker, puffing out his little pigeon chest. But nowt got done. Least, not till my Billy cocked his toes. Then, not only did *they* knock down the inside wall, oh, no. They flattened the whole flaming street, and all!

Egged on by that Doctor Forster, I bet – obviously *one o' them*. Course, he wears an ear-ring! Pushing all us old sticks into a block o' flats what we didn't want, and what no-one else wanted, neither. 'Won't get me in there!' I flaming well told 'em. 'With all them steps for climbing? Cod's wallop!'

Always on the move, that's you, Agnes. Always mouthing off – just like your Billy. A cobbler what worked for a firm of other old cobblers - ! Big fella, he was. Like a house-end. Knew a thing or two 'bout things, he did. Like me. No knowing what he didn't know, lad like him, on the quiet.

Nor did, neither. So blow him, I thought. And off I'd go of an evening, singing and playing the old Joanna in all the pubs and other places of entertainment. Everything from Chopin to *Kitten on the Keys*. Everyone looked to Agnes, they did, for a good old-fashioned 'knees-up'. 'Mother Brown' they called me, even though I never did have no kids - 'cept for the little girl, so they said. Sally, I'd have called her – like in the song -.

Always plenty o' walking round these parts? Yer can say that again. For keeping *them* off me back. When it's real cold, there's the Public Library like I said. Nice, warm in there. Me screwmatics, see. Especially when the wind blows – with the snow coming down horizontal.

Have a free read of the papers and that. Even p'raps of the *Dancing Times* – nice, that is – if Councillor Mel Parker hasn't nicked it for his missus – Fenella – who'll have the best legs in the graveyard when time comes. Read anything in there, yer can. If it's boring though, it'll put you asleep. Then they turn you out. Snow or no snow - .

'You get up. You fall down. Meanwhile, you keep dancing.' Something I read once, in the Public Library.

It's after dark I don't like. Spend the night in the park here, sometimes. Least, I did do. In that old summer-house over there – see? Hid behind them sycamores. Nice, comfortable. Like a sort of love-nest. Least, it might've been, till yobs

Mr Arthur Bourchier
as Henry VIII

dumped these needle-things and empty spray-cans inside.
Then vandals burned it down. But *'You keep dancing'* –

Course, he led me a bit of a dance, did my Billy. He were
a good husband. Put me in hospital, he did. Brings me back

from the pub, one night –

'I love you, our Ag,' he says. 'I love you. And I'm mad at all them others what've loved you! And all them what's going to love you.' Then he bashed me 'cross the head with the sweeper. And I had twelve stitches. He were ever so good to me.

Eh – yer what ? - Locking gates for the night? Right – hold on. Hold on!

4 LOIS
Neighbour From Hell

Excuse me popping my head over the garden hedge. I know we haven't spoken yet, you having just moved in. I'm Lois, by the way. I wonder if you'd mind turning down your radio – just a bit. It'll do when you go in. It's on account of Adrian, you see. He – and Kelly – have a lie-in every Sunday. I insist on it. Rest and relaxation, it's a sacred trust when you've got a child, I've always felt.

I remember saying that to Dada when we'd tried for a family for ten years and it looked as though we weren't meant to have one. That Providence obviously didn't think he was up to it. He took it very hard. And then, would you believe, along came Adrian. It was a little miracle. It nearly killed me though - two months early, and he was very fragile. I've had to give him lots of extra special care always.

And people laugh now about measles, but it's no joke if you nearly lose your little miracle. We almost lost ours at five. But I've made it up to him, whether he's wanted it or not.

He works really hard you know, four and a half days a week at Fatima's Florals. He creates windows for most of the big stores in town. They're not like any other windows you ever see. A true artist, that's what he is - but when you've got a genius to contend with, they can be a bit touchy.

He set his mind when he was nineteen on something fast. A Jensen Interceptor. He thought that would reflect his professional status. And I suppose he would have been able

Master Eric Ray as Prince Zara and Miss Julia Neilson as Queen Frederique in The Popinjay

to afford it – eventually. But he had to have wheels there and then, so I told Dada we'd sacrifice the Skoda. I insisted. Not a thought for ourselves, Adrian had got to have it.

We never mention that night. But he never did it again – Adrian, I mean. Of course, he was only learning the trade then. He settled down a bit more when he got promoted – that was his thirtieth birthday, gave us two reasons for celebrating. Although, I worried about the stress - would it be too much for him. After his promotion, you see, he had to think as well.

Now with Kelly, it was quite different. The background and everything. She was just an office assistant, twenty-four when Adrian brought her home the first time. But as I said to Dada, at twenty-four, a woman's practically mature, she should be able to fend for herself.

I suppose she tried to. She was very bubbly, got a lot of ideas in her head. I felt personally that she had a lot of growing up to do, though. Adrian even said she'd been talking about a mortgage. Well, she soon learned. Because we don't have scenes in our family.

And all that bubbling – soon wore off. Nowadays, she's like skimmed milk, hardly ever goes out. Gave her job up – not much of a loss though, it was only something in the office. Agoraphobia, they call it. Just 'nerves', if you ask me. Sympathy with that sort of thing only makes people worse. It gives them encouragement. You have to be hard, or else you end up being as neurotic as they are.

But of course, some people cannot appreciate how vital it is to be there in the right way for your children. Only the other lunch-time at work - I'm in catering at Cassons

Engineering - I'd been showing the kitchen staff the latest photos of Adrian. Adrian - and Kelly - in the garden. Adrian - and Kelly - in the Skoda. Adrian - and Kelly - on the dry ski slope. Adrian - and Kelly - in the whirlpool at the Swimming Baths.

I heard Madge Kingsley - the supervisor, she's so common, shout: 'It's about time Lois and Ted stopped smothering that lad of theirs!' – just as a group of workers came in from Precision Ball-bearings for their Toad in the Hole, or Organic Cauliflower Cheese (both with chips and two veg). Guilt on her part, pure and simple. Just trying to make excuses for the way she's neglected her Alex. And look what's happened to him!!

It's not as though I ever tried to stand in Adrian's way. After he was promoted, they wanted to send him abroad – and I encouraged him to go. He went to Paris. A very nasty experience. He found that no-one spoke so that he could understand them. In the end, he was glad to get home, glad to be back with all of us.

Well, don't let me keep you – from turning down the radio, I mean. Thanks so much. Iris and Bob were always very good about it. Not like the Gurneys on the other side. But of course, they didn't last long.

Sunday evenings, Adrian – and Kelly – stay in now. As I said to Dada, why should they bother to go out when they've got their best friends here? We like a game of whist or bridge. But Kelly – well, you know – so we're always looking for somebody to make up a foursome.

You don't play cards? Not to worry – you'll soon learn.

*Mr Lewis Waller as Col. Cyril Egerton
in The Fires of Fate*

Miss Viola Tree as Sleeping Beauty
in Pinkie and the Fairies

Mrs Patrick Campbell
as Bella Donna

Miss Maud Allan as Salome

5 ARABELLA
Siren Song

Ah, English tourists! Welcome, English tourists, to Wernerberg Castle, Wernerberg-on-the-Rhine. You have been reading in your Guide Books about our river – the Rhine? Ah yes, it is beautiful river - but dangerous.

Look over the rail of my terrace, here as we drink our wine in the sun – *ja?* Look how it swirls down there, the water, all around the Lurlei Rock. Upon that rock once sang a beautiful maiden – a nymph all in white with stars in her long hair. And why did she sing? She sing to lure the boatmen and the travellers what pass along the river to a watery grave.

Her voice, it was legend. And so also was mine. For I am Arabella von Stamitz, I am the greatest opera singer in the world. This you know. The whole world, she knows. But I tell you – and you tell nobody – my name when I was born, it was not Arabella von Stamitz, it was Inger Blumer. But Inger Blumer, it is plain, and so I am Arabella von Stamitz.

I was the toast of every Opera House in Europe, and in America. I had letters of congratulations from President Truman, from Bob Hope, Vivien Leigh – from Marlene – from Noel Coward. The walls of my Banqueting Hall, they are covered. Photographs signed – not all signed by myself either. Toscanini – Furtwangler – Klemperer – Gigli – and my hero – ah! The great Errol Flynn!

When I was twenty-one, I was the great new *wunderkind.* The composer Richard Strauss, he drank champagne from my glass slipper at the Gala of Rossini's *Cinderella* when the War, it was just finished. He was an old man, but he was very sexy. He was my Prince Charming.

My feet were tiny, but the whole of Europe knows the story of how I walked, when I was eighteen – penniless – from my home village to Vienna. There was chaos everywhere, people moving en masse, hither and thither, and everywhere the Allied Forces and the Americans. How they – what do you say? – whistle like the wolf at me, because I was very beautiful. They offered me lifts in their lorries and jeeps – and nylons – and chewing-gum – but poof! I was a good girl. I walked!

Then – Vienna at last. Number 10, Bunkstrasse. I knocked. No answer. What would you? I sat down on the step and I sang 'One Fine Day' from *Madama Butterfly*. The door – it burst open. There he stood, the most famous voice trainer in Austria.

He glared at me.

'No buskers!'

I was not impressed. He was solid, barrel-chested, little man in lederhosen.

'I'm hungry,' I told him.

But he was not impressed either. He told me: 'So am I.' Then, after a pause: 'Hokay, you better come in.'

But in two weeks only, I was out again. He had, he said, nothing else he could teach me. The voice, he said, was all that mattered. And my voice, it was already perfect.

Miss Lily Brayton as Clotilde and Mr Oscar Asche
as Count Hannibal in Count Hannibal

So with his recommendation and my beauty, I took the world by storm. A diva! I sang and men threw themselves at my feet to die. Or to take me out to supper. Or to present me with jewels and flowers. Or to proposition me...

Or to marry me. I married three times – once for money, once for my title – and once for love. They were all disasters – the men, not the marriages. But I was not born to be a wife. I was born to be a widow – the Merry Widow, that was my role. By public demand. But was I not perfect also in tragedy – as Tosca, Lady Macbeth, Carmen?

In the spring, I cruised around the Greek Islands. In summer – my schedules bulging – I was seen at Cannes and St. Tropaz. I out-Callas Callas. I had *many* lovers, rich, sun-tanned – young and old. The young now old, the old now dead – from exhaustion. But me – never!

And I do not work for Battered Brides, nor knit for the Third World. Pah! Nor even, like Bardot, do I make a home for the animals and the donkeys. No! I write my memoirs, I teach – even though the young are squeakers and the old are squawkers. My role now, I am the local chanteuse. I give the occasional concert for charity – Schubert, Mahler, Wagner ('*Das Lieberstot', naturellement*), Gershwin and Cole Porter. With them it does not matter if I forget the words.

I am an old woman, no? The mind, you think, it is not what it was. As for the beauty, we will not talk about the beauty. But ah – the voice.

Oh, the voice! It is still there – the magic! Only this morning, they tell me, they pulled from the river, the body of another young, handsome boatman. So many have been so tragically drowned - by the Lorelei.

Mr Robert Loraine as Mr Clement Parbury and
Miss Ethel Irving as Mrs Parbury in The Tyranny of Tears

6 FRANNY
Chasing Rainbows

I can't believe it. I just can't. Seems like everything's turning out exactly like a fairy story.

I'm going to tell you exactly how it happened. It started when we were having our dinner today. Boris – that's my husband – finished off the jar of pickles, breathing fire as he stared all round my lovely dining-room.

'I'm brassed off at seeing my face in these brasses,' he growled at the wall.

Well, for the whole week, my Borrie had had a mood on him, since the haulage firm he worked for had made him redundant. He'd been driving thirty years – always punctual, no accidents – since before we were married. And now here he was hanging about, everywhere in my way when I had to get the housework done.

'I'm brassed off with *this* place and all,' he said. I was doing the washing up and he came striding into the kitchen, ex-rugby player, with the *Exchange and Mart* under his arm. 'So are *you*, Franny. Brassed off too. Be honest with yourself."

'That's rubbish,' I told him. I had to hold onto the sink, I was in shock.

'Middle-age drift, that's been the trouble for a long time,' he said, 'between me and you.'

He was right. It wasn't my fault, though. All the years I'd kept everywhere like a stately house, and he'd hardly been here, one way or the other.

'This could be our fresh chance, start all over again, Franny.' The washing-up water went cold. He took hold of my hand. He lifted it to his lips. 'What d'yer say, girl?'

I was too gob-smacked to say anything. Took me back years. Borrie and me – we used to look at each other like that once – I suppose it was our hormones. And being young and squeaky clean, just like that metal bin we had, before these plastic wheelies everyone raves about now. No-one else's metal bin ever shone like *ours*.

Then he sat me down by the table.

'This is it - the chance of a life-time," he said, opening the *Exchange* and *Mart* and pointing to the small ads.

Miss Hutin Britton as Nancy in Oliver Twist

'Fully-furbished cooker, fridge, rear-facing kitchen,' it read. 'Immobiliser/alarm, 2-berth, wardrobes, mains hook-up – Volkswagen camper van. What d'you reckon to life on the open road?'

'It's got to be his withdrawal symptoms,' I thought. '*That's what it's all about.*'

Because this wasn't the first time, you see. Last year, for our holidays, he'd pushed for Vladivostok – by hot-air balloon. And he hired a horse-drawn gypsy caravan, the year before that. Now I've nothing against the countryside, but I'm not a country person. Nor a horse person. And all that rain. And those sodden narrow lanes. How can you get dry in a gypsy caravan? How on earth did the gypsies manage? I couldn't help feeling sorry for the horse, either.

I tried to remind Borrie but he wouldn't let me interrupt.

'It'll be a lot different with a camper van,' he said, and there was a warm something in his voice that meant *more* than adventure. 'It could be like a second honeymoon, Frannie, *you'll* see.'

Well, I was really glad I was sitting down, I was shaking that much. 'What about our lovely home?' I tried to ask, but he swept that aside with a wave of his arm.

'We'll take it with us. Least, some of it. Life in a camper van, you'll only need to do a *bit* of cleaning.' He was laughing at me like he used to in the old days. But my only thought was 'Oh, I wish he'd just leave it alone.'

'The owner's accepted my offer. I went and looked, yesterday,' he said, and he punching the air – I think they call it a High Five. 'Passion wagon – here we come.'

Mr Walter Passmore and child

Then he gave me a big hug that made me gasp. 'Lay off, Borrie. I'm fighting for breath.'

'Like the *first* time we clapped eyes on one another eh, girl?' he roared. Like a lion. Then he whirled out of the kitchen, and before I could gather myself together, he'd changed into tracksuit trousers, sweat-shirt and trainers, stuck his baseball cap on his head, and went stomping down the hall – he was always a fit man, despite his size. The pictures rattled on the walls as he banged the front door after him.

I told myself I could breathe easy. But could I? It was all too much.

'I've got the copper and brass for cleaning, and picture-rails to dust,' I thought. 'And the garden's only small but somebody has to keep it tidy.'

I mean, passing along the street, folk notice. Especially Sundays, when they're going to Church next door. I've always liked that idea. It's not many who can boast they've got Jesus for a neighbour.

I've often wondered whether *He* ever notices. I do like to think He's around. Borrie says I think too much. He once joked I was like 'The iron fist in the rubber glove'. At least I suppose it was a joke. I never have been bossy. Only one thing I insisted on – he took off his overalls and work-boots at the back door, because I can't stand the smell of diesel oil. He was always good about it too, though he can get shirty at times. Like one day, I gave him a feather duster, for him to give me a hand. And he let out a yell just like a Samurai warrior, and he hurled it through the open window – the feather duster, I mean - and brought down his ham fist on the mahogany dining-table, like he was trying to cut it in two. All he did was hurt his fist – drew blood, so it was a good job the cloth was still on. And the feather duster'd cost all of fifty pee in the market.

I suppose I can't always understand his jokes.

He's got a serious side too though. Chairman of the Thursday Night Quiz Team at *The Whistlers' Arms,* Captain of both the Bowls and Skittles teams. And he referees for the Youth League Football. Says it keeps him young at heart.

He spends a lot of time with his old school-mate, Ken Colesworth and Olive, his wife. She's really nice. I get on well with them both. Borrie seems to laugh a lot when he's with them, though. They have a strange effect on him.

One time he came home from seeing them and I mentioned about my kitchen floor being clean enough to eat our meal off. 'Let's try it, then,' he says, and threw two cushions down. 'Let's get back to nature.'

Well, I don't know how it happened. But we ended up rolling around on the kitchen floor, rubbing one another all over with Fairy Liquid. Bubbles, all colours of the rainbow,

Mr Harry Fragson as Mlle. Lisette in Washing A Babe at the Drury Lane Pantomime

you remember from when you were a child.

He's a bit like a child himself, Borrie. I think he'd have liked children. But I couldn't have coped with the place like a tip. 'Sides, they said my hormones wouldn't run to it. In fact, I ran the other way, instead.

Oh, I've seen Borrie give the glad-eye to one or two. But I've never been one of these ho-ho-ho sort of girls. I listen to my old Bing Crosby records when I've got the time. *Samantha, I'm Dreaming of a White Christmas*, and *The Bells of St. Mary's*. Audrey Fyffer and her friends across the street, they rave about Danny O' Donnell. But Bing, he's good enough for me. I don't go to Church, but I do like to hear *The Bells of St. Mary's*.

They've always had a lot of music at the Colesworth's. Used to be rock n' roll. Now it's the grandchildren, mostly with what do they call it? Rapping and hopping. Ken and Olive never had hormone problems. They never seem to have any sort of problems, actually, even though you can't help noticing how dirty their lace curtains always are, and the dust over everything. They seem just to *laugh* it off. Even the dirty dishes piled up in the sink. They've had an overflow for thirty years! And Ken a plumber.

I've always tried hard, you know. I never mention to Borrie about the wind in *my* pipes, and Polisher's Elbow, Housemaid's Knee, my gippy hip, and the fact that it's blue *murder* holding the floor mop sometimes, let alone the vacuum-cleaner. When I do the spring cleaning, I can hardly move the furniture.

'An iron fist in a rubber glove'? I'm more like Little Polly Flinders, sat among the cinders. Or at least, that's what it *used* to feel like. What it's felt like for years, really. Until now, when everything seems to have turned into a fairy story. Since Borrie went out, I've been feeling really funny. As though someone else has come into the room. There's this lovely warmth everywhere, feels like it's going right through me. And a dazzling sort of light all around – brighter than my best polishing, even.

It's a kind of sunshine, just like on our holiday abroad, the time we went to Majorca. Well, perhaps the Neighbour did notice me, after all.

'A fresh chance, a fresh start.' Well, Borrie said that, didn't he? And I think he's right. It could be, couldn't it? We could be holding hands somewhere, watching the tide come in, with the wind blowing through our hair. Foam, bubbles everywhere – all the colours of the rainbow - .

Now, how did I come to miss that cobweb on the table-leg? I'll get the duster. Oh, but they've been washed, I've just remembered, and hung out on the line. I'll put them with the soap and scrubbing-brush, once they've dried. All ready for the camper van. With the rest of the luggage. Not forgetting the Fairy Liquid, of course....!

Miss Phyllis Bedells

Miss Anna Pavlova

7 MARILYN
Fairy Dumbbell

'Once more it is the magic time
For joy and fun and pantomime.
The Demon King will smirk and leer,
But not to worry – I am here!'

Isn't it pathetic? The best my new scriptwriter can do –
and listen to this –

'Fairy Gossamer is my name,
I sparkle through the wind and rain,
And yet – oh, if the truth I tell,
I'm so fat, they call me Fairy Dumbbell!'

That's always been the big joke when people have written
scripts for me – my size. You think they'd try and think of
something different. When I was at Drama School, some
clever clogs tried sticking pins in me, saying I'd go bang and
disappear, or go down slowly, making a rude noise all the
way. Said it would make the most marvellous cabaret act.

Another suggestion best forgotten was that I called myself
the *Sugar Ton Fairy!* I could have cried. But as a trouper, you
learn to take it all with a smile. As another of my script-
writers put it:

'When you're in Show Business like me,
You learn to turn that magic key,
You take the cat-calls and the jeers
And sing and dance away your tears.'

Oh, I could squirm sometimes, though!

Miss Camille Clifford and Mr Farren Soutar

Right, well let's get down to business. Pantomime, Christmas plays, even Shakespeare – '*The Dream*', of course – yes, I've done the lot. And I've never appeared in cabaret. I've done guest appearances – graced children's Book Fairs, parties – and regularly fluttered my wings in Santa's Grotto. My speciality's feeding the reindeer.

Thrill upon thrill, I made the Royal Variety Performance in '94, as part of the corps de ballet – didn't have to dance, but posed in the background. Part of a tableau of Greek nymphs, would you believe!

Course, being a theatrical pro, I've played many other parts in my time. But being a sprite is my speciality. I really make it pay, being Fairy Dumbbell. There's all the little extras, like being taken up by firms for advertising, and costume turns at business dos and dinners. My real name's Marilyn, actually. After Marilyn Monroe. My mother worshipped

Miss Cecily Courtneidge as Miyo Ko San in Mousmé

Marilyn – saw all her films. I rather like it myself – and I make a point of always keeping my own hair really *golden blonde!*

Now my sister, who's much older, is called Lily. Quite plain. But she found herself a very good professional name – it's better known than mine, actually. Got in with this chap, he was called Count Vivaldi then, and they formed a new illusionist act together. They played all the popular resorts for years – even toured the continent, went to Paris, Brussels, Rome pulling rabbits and pigeons and canaries out of thin air. To show they'd got nothing up their sleeves, they didn't wear any. In fact, that was their gimmick. They wore nothing at all, except for four fig-leaves between them. Called themselves Adam and Eve. And they had this trick to round off their act – one clap of Adam's hands, they'd both disappear. Worked a treat, except one time something went wrong. He clapped and the fig-leaves disappeared, leaving them there, large as life and twice as natural, you might say. They lost a bit of their bravura after that.

The critics make fools of themselves over my sister, but it's only because she's thin. Well, I was as thin as her once. Theatrical digs were the problem, especially the ones in Blackpool. The land-ladies and their Lancashire Hot-pots. But my real downfall came in 'Mrs O' Brien's Kitchen' – small café down our High Street. The cakes….the trifles…!

Mrs O' Brien comes from County Clare – and by all the saints now, wouldn't you know it? I said to her:

'Sure, tis a shameful thing you do,
Keep feeding me your Irish Stew.
Me calories, they break the scale –
I'm getting bigger than a whale.'

53

Well, I've never claimed to be a poet – that's why I employ a script-writer.

In the course of my theatrical career, I've played the Good Fairy – I've played the Wicked Fairy – I've played the Fairy Queen – I've played Titania's Fairy Handmaiden – I've played Santa's Little Fairy Helper - . And one year, when they were short, I doubled as an angel. But there's one part I've never yet played, and it's my lifetime's ambition.

I want to be the Fairy on the Top of the Christmas Tree.

No, I'm serious. I've even been going to Weight Watchers, as well as attending the gym regularly. The Fairy on the Christmas Tree – she is *the* part. Nothing to do, of course. But you're seen everywhere. Like a super-model. I'm really determined, and I'm not going to give up. I've already lost half a stone.

Well, got to hurry along – another audition, actually. As my script-writer would say:

'The clock has tolled the midnight chime
And as in every pantomime
The Ball is over, I must fly –
My taxi meter's clicking by –

It's been so grand to meet you all:
Let's keep in touch – give me a call,
And let my agent, Mr Carey,
Know if you ever need a fairy:

And hopefully, a slimmer me
Will see you next year – on the tree!'

Miss Pauline Chase

8 MARTHA
Mrs Dracula

Why, hello Doctor Stevens. Lovely to see you again. Are you enjoying the party?

And Mrs Stevens? I didn't recognise you dear, how different you look. So much younger than I remember...How many years is it?...

Pardon, Doctor? Oh it's *Andrea*, not Hilda, is it? So pleased to meet you, Andrea. I'm Martha Parrott, an old, old friend...I say, you can rely on me, I shan't give you away...

Oh yes, I've known your Doctor Stevens since we were all young things together...Flavia was one of our set too, our hostess. Just look at her over there, she's positively bubbling, isn't she? – so youthful, circulating, chatting – amazing really, when you think of that man she married...

Did you ever meet him, Andrea? Oh, lucky escape...

I expect it's all put on with Flavia, dear...either that or she's taking off, if you know what I mean...No, they try to keep it very quiet - . But if there's mineral water in that glass, I'll be very surprised...

Mutual friend? Oh, Flavia's everybody's mutual friend... or should the word be 'common'?...It's quite a moot point, isn't it?....but then, I've always thrived on debate...

Oh, but we've hardly started to chat, Doctor.... Do you know, I always seem to get the impression that people can't wait to get away from me! And I can't imagine why, unless

Mr Arthur Bourchier and Miss Violet Vanbrugh

they think I'm collecting for a good cause...

I see that's brought a smile, Andrea. And that's good, because I do think we should really enter into everything, take an interest... I love to get excited about all sorts of topics...

Pardon my being personal, but you look a little green, dear...Feeling sick? ...I suppose you're not – no, of course not, not at the Doctor's age. But life is so marvellous, isn't it? – surprises around every corner...

Some people complain about having a problem with hyper-active children, seems to be the fashion these days – but what's wrong with being on the go? Do you know, Andrea, I'm hyper-active myself, and I positively *thrive* on it. Remember Maurice, Doctor? – my husband, Andrea – he's such a joker, claims I've given him more ulcers than ten children would have...

But I think it's so true that if you don't use it, you lose it. The brain, I mean. I've got no intention of going ga-ga...can you imagine anything worse, Andrea?..

Alertness of the brain, it runs in the family. Now my mother, Andrea, is eighty-two, and she has completed five romantic novels and three slim volumes of verse in five years....oh, heavens, no, not for publication, she's far too modest, entirely for her own amusement....But she keeps herself busy banging away on the computer with complete artistry – she might just as well be playing Beethoven's *Hammerclavier Sonata,* or the *Warsaw Concerto - .*

No, alas, my own gifts do not extend to writing novels or performing concertos. I'm just an old-fashioned little thing ...you'll agree with me there, I'm sure, Doctor! - but I am an inveterate letter-writer, you know. I write letters to *The Times, The Observer, Woman's Own* – any periodical there is to hand. I even fax the *Beano* – it keeps me feeling young....

Something else I've inherited from Cecilia – my mother, Andrea – because she wrote letters before she decided to be

Miss Clara Evelyn as Jana Van Raalte in
The Girl in the Train

a novelist....Oh, yes, she wrote to the Queen, and the Prime Minister, and the President of the United States – and the Pope. And do you know, they all acknowledged them instantly...though, I think she's still waiting for some word from the Pope – the last but one...

She's always bursting with energy, says it's the fault of that little bottle of elixir that you prescribe for her, Doctor. Swears by it. Well, figuratively speaking, because Cecilia never swears....

You know, I've always felt that you were blessed with the gift of good listening, Doctor; that's why it's such a joy to talk to you....I say, do you feel all right? You look very fraught...Too many sleepless nights – you need to prescribe yourself a little bottle of that elixir ... though I'm sure Andrea's far too young to know about things like that - .

What fun it would be to be a fly on the wall at The Furze!...I bet your house is buzzing with activity now...But you have to remember, Doctor, you're not as young as you were sixty years ago....

I say, why don't I write a letter to the papers about you both – it's such a romantic story –

Oh, Andrea! Quick, Doctor, I think you'd better get her to the bathroom. Are you quite sure she's not...?

Well! He looks in just as much of a hurry as she does. Must be something they've eaten....

Why...Hello, Professor Dawes! So lovely to see you – and Mrs Dawes. You look ever so young, dear – how many years must it.......?

THE LADIES PUT ON
THEIR FINERY....

Miss Gabriel Ray

Mrs L. Waller

Miss Emmy Wehlen

Miss Marie Lohr

Miss Ethel Barrymore

.... FOR EVERY OCCASION

Miss Pauline Chase

III

THE MEN OUT DO THEM....

Mr Matheson Lang as Petruchio in The Taming of the Shrew

Mr Lewis Waller

IV

9 MADDY
Paw-paws and Passion Fruit

Fifty-six years of age, and half my life had passed by when I first set eyes on Zak. A tall, good-looking young gentleman - about twenty-two I imagined - fumbling through the odds and ends on my haberdashery stall in the market.

'Can I help, sir?' I ventured.

'Got a pair of silver briefs, Ma?' he grinned, but he wasn't a bit self-conscious as he pushed back a thick lock of blond hair from his face. 'Or a thong – even better.'

'And what are you in?' I asked. 'Show business?'

He just grinned a bit more. 'I've got a lot worth showing.'

I thought fast.

'And what about an audience?' I heard myself saying. 'Maybe a one-woman audience?'

He could think just as fast as me. I could tell he understood. His eyes went very blue.

'You're on,' he said.

Well, I can spot talent when I see it, and that boy definitely had something – and it wasn't just star quality! The next morning, he moved in.

So after thirty yawning years of hawking haberdashery, I threw up the business – the business Alf and me had started when we were first married. I made a very nice profit – at

Mr Matheson Lang as Romeo

long last. Alf had always been more of a hindrance than a help, and in the end, we had a flaming row on the stall, just one of many.

'Drop dead!' I told him – and he did. What a shock! He'd actually done something somebody told him for once in his life.

And then, well, I was on my own – until Zak showed up. A drama student at the university. And he needed somewhere decent to stay – so I bought a nice retirement bungalow, near my sister-in-law's, as it happened – but so what?

Zak seemed to fit in right from day one. And having him around, it was a bit like having Steve McQueen. I always fancied Steve McQueen. He'd do little things – like buying me flowers. Even though I paid for them. He surprised me. And I've always liked surprises, since ever. And he'd link arms in public.

Irma – that's my sister-in-law – she didn't like it one bit. She'd stick her perm up over the hedge from three doors up and call me flighty. 'And with all that hanky-panky,' she'd shout, 'you're doomed to Purgatory, Maddy Unsworth!'

'Huh! I was in that when I was married to your Alf!' I shouted back. '*And* not enough hanky-panky, either. I've got a lot of catching up to do. So you can keep those sour grapes, Irm, I'm into paw-paws and passion fruit.'

Well, you should have seen her face. Plain jealous.

Then we had the parties, with Zak's friends coming round from Media Studies and the Music Department. And not all pop. Garcia played the flamenco guitar, and Maria sang 'Ave Maria' to the didgeridoo, and Rastus – well, I just didn't believe Rastus when I first saw him – six foot six, in tribal tattoos and dreadlocks. He used to get carried away playing rap, sometimes till two in the morning.

Of course, the neighbours kicked up – we were even the subject of a petition. But they were all just plain jealous. Who wouldn't be?

63

In summer there were the barbies. Talk about sizzling! When the lads found I hadn't got a patio, they built one. Oh, they really showed me how to enjoy life – and how to spend my money. Particularly Zak. A bit different to when Alf and I first met in Blackpool. He promised me the moon, but he only gave me hell all those years.

So it seemed only fair that I should give Zak a bit of a hand up. And when you've worked the markets for as long as I have, you get to know what's what.

I got him started with some photo sessions, built up his portfolio – and modelling fun wear for a catalogue. Then, he had to have an agent. I called up Des in Manchester, got him bookings in the clubs, and even doing hen parties. He only had to flex his pecs and they went wild.

You might think I'd have been jealous, the way those hens tried to tear him apart. But I was the one who took him home, and patched him up with old-fashioned brown liniment – amongst other things. I used to get more than a flex of the pecs – and then I'd have to patch him up all over again.

'Maddy,' he'd say. 'Thanks.' And that was all I wanted.

It wasn't long before he was on the telly. Zak versus the Gladiators – you remember? And he won! Well, I knew he would. But it meant, of course, that I had to let him go. I couldn't have stood in his way – not when Theresa, his producer, made it clear that she wanted to give him 'personal coaching'.

He still writes to me, though, and I try not to dwell on it. The fact that he's gone. But I am developing other interests.

For instance, any time at all, Luigi promised to drop in. One of Zak's friends from Media Studies as a matter of fact. Lean. Mean. Like a young Marlon Brando. And I always fancied Marlon Brando.

Sir Henry Irving

10 BESSIE
Love for Sale

'You shall at dawn, be taken to an appointed place and there hanged by the neck, thence buried at the cross-roads, with a stake driven through your heart...'

....or so His Lordship had the nerve to tell me! I mean, in this day and age – it's 18th November, 1685, that I'm living in, after all, even though technology has made it possible for you Ladies and Gentlemen of the Twenty-first Century Press to visit me here in my 'virtual condemned cell'. Why shouldn't we have press conferences even in the Seventeenth Century? The world needs to know, that's what I say!

News of the World? –oh, delighted, I'm sure. Yes, I'll tell you everything. It was just the sort of scene your readers will know so well – hooligans, sex and violence, the lot. With all that shouting, it sounded like Judge Jeffries was auditioning for a Hammer horror film, or something.

As for the mob – oh, sorry, jury (well, there's not much difference!) – they stood up, jeering and clapping. And the gentlefolk in the Public Gallery, they were yowling as well, as I tried to make a dignified exit. A couple of smelly young roughs in uniforms were pushing and shoving against each shoulder. Even my chains were rattling and clanking like in some B-movie ghost story.

A death sentence, I ask you! Where's the justice in that? Same as I told the court, everyone knows I'm a witch – national and international – to be seen at Psychic Fairs the length and breadth of the country. And I've written books on the subject. The latest – my *Almanac of Spells and Potions* – Book of the Month, a proven European best-seller!

At which point, Judge Jeffries – a lovely-looking man – not shouting this time, he even asked if the courtroom was big enough to take me. I said Yes, of course, and everyone laughed their silly heads off.

'*Another* bristle to the proverbial broomstick!' I thought. That of a stand-up comedienne?

'Where's the contract to sign me up for a chat-show of my own on the box?' I asked – though no-one seemed to know what I meant. More laughter.

Then Judge Jeffries asked me to read aloud from *Bessie's Almanac* – which I did, gladly. And no word of a lie, I had every one of that lot in the palm of this very hand. Listening, spellbound!

It was then, Ladies and Gentlemen, I felt he'd taken a bit of a liking to me. Or to what you'd call my *charisma*. I could see that bright, mischievous glint in his eye. No – you might grin – but that's the honest truth, that is.

Some call him 'the Hanging Judge' – or even Judge Dredd, like the cartoon character - but there's nothing funny about His Lordship, I can tell you. Prosecutor *and* judge in the treason trials of Lord William Russell and Algernon Sidney, a few years back – sensational Seventeenth Century equivalents of the O. J. Simpson trial in America, in case you didn't know. Convicted and executed the pair of them!

Oh, real earnest, that's Judge Jeffries. I mean – despite his liking me, he's passed sentence on me, just the same.

Miss Camille Clifford

Men – they're so unpredictable, aren't they? It was thanks to one of them – the old Duke of – Where's-it – I ended up in the dock. He complained that my Love Potion No 9 - (de luxe) – with powdered horn of unicorn – (advertised world-wide) – *did not work* for Cordelia, his vivacious young Duchess.

Mr Fred Terry and Miss Alice Crawford in
Matt of Merrymount

'But it did!' I told the court. 'Her Grace eloped with a lusty young steward of the bed-chamber. The same to be said for many a woman who's maybe found favour, say, with some life-saver beach boy instead of an older, lack-lustre husband!

'And why not?' I said. 'You can't get water if the well's run dry!' Gasps from around the court! Then some lean, smarmy type from Temple Bar suggested that I had no respect for the sanctity of marriage. Me – Bessie Cauldwell, who's lived to bury three husbands!!!

'I simply sell love to all,' I said. 'But what they do with it is *their* business, darling!'

Then, uproar! Everyone shouted at everyone else. Judge Jeffries shouted even louder, to shut them up – and then pronounced my writings, spells and potions to be creations of the devil. And me, guilty of witchcraft. No messing.

70

Dawn's not so early in November – but why wait till then? Because there has been what you might call a *development.* Displaying that unpredictability of all men, same as I mentioned, a certain person quietly passed a parchment to the Court Usher after the trial – *this note!*

....*For me!* In which he says he must see me here at midnight – the witching hour! And I think there are only a few minutes to go. Mmmm – now, let me see ....

After such a long, hard day passing sentences, I'm sure he'll want to relax – so what more effective than a nice cup of tea! And I can guarantee he'll feel even better when I've mixed in the contents of *this* satchet. My Love Potion No 9 – (de luxe) etc, etc.

Just think, Ladies and Gentlemen of the Press – I'll be able to use a new advert – *'as recommended – by Judge Jeffries!'*

*Miss Lily Elsie as Sonia and Mr Joseph Coyne as
Count Danilo in The Merry Widow*

11 MOYA
Kiss of Death

Verity and Christian are two of my oldest friends. They were married twenty-five years ago yesterday. Naturally, I sent them a card, but I couldn't resist giving them a tinkle as well.

'Oh, Moya!' Verity wept.

She said they were tears of joy. She said everything was coming up roses – but I could see through that. Roses can have nasty thorns, I thought.

'I'm on my way,' I told her.

I'm always prepared for that sort of thing, because other people's lives seem to get in such a mess. I don't know how it happens. I told her to meet the early train at Crewe. So here I am - holdall in tow, ready for action!

Last time, I was so concerned I caught the milk train, and decided to spend the extra time going round the Charity Shops – because I always try to support charities fully. Anyway, it just so happened that I met Verity, who was in Crewe long before she was supposed to meet me.

She said she was 'getting her courage up'. To tell me the sordid details, I suppose.

We had a cup of coffee together, and then she drove me back. And when we got there, we found Christian practically *leaning* on this poor woman in the garden. Well, I know what *I* saw – and *she* was mortified, as you'd expect. But he had the face to try and claim he was only explaining how to prune the clematis!

Miss Constance Collier and Mr Beerbohm Tree

Well, the two of them – Christian and Verity – came in for some nitty-gritty counselling from yours truly, I can tell you. Especially him. He just sat there and took it, very laid back. Then Verity suddenly burst out that I was to leave him alone and clear out. She actually called me an interfering old busy-body. Of course, I understood. She was in trauma. But him – bare-faced as they make them.

Too many people are just like that. I could tell you about Trish Tryner. She's the daughter of another of my old friends, Marge Allman that was. Of course, she does live in Camden. When Marge and I went, what with all these foreign men in and out of the house, you could see what sort of a set-up they were running – and the place swarming with children. Trish had the face to try and claim they were nothing to do with her.

But that house was just like the United Nations – and she seemed quite proud of it. More like the Zen of

Claustrophobia, I told her. Because at least two of the brood were of Oriental persuasion - so I had a few sharp words to say at this Mr Chang, when he showed his face, in my best Chinese accent.

He seemed to fly into a rage. I couldn't understand a word, of course. Then Lazlo, the Hungarian from the basement flat – I'd hardly opened my mouth – and he did the same thing. Highly strung, these Hungarians!

On the top floor, they were from Jamaica. I was very polite to this Winston, even though he didn't look as if he could understand English. I was right, because he simply went crashing back upstairs and went wild on the voodoo drums, or oil drums, or whatever kind of drums they were. Then that woke up some army of snotty-nosed infants. And Trish screamed at me. She said that I was just a frustrated old bag and I caused chaos wherever I went.

I understood. You can start your mid-life crisis at twenty, you know.

People say to me: 'You're always trying to help others. Why don't you think about yourself for a change? Why don't you get married?'

I was asked. Mr Andrew McAllister was his name, from Edinburgh. He used to call me his 'wee gal'. Me – wee! Mind, he had the size of an Angus bull - though not the roar, in spite of the red hair and beard. But he was always – well, trying to *touch* me. He must have thought I would like that sort of thing.

Perverted, I call it. I could never have married him.

So he married someone else. On the rebound.

He couldn't have understood me at all. He was a Calvinist - and I have two gay budgies. I had to part with the little blue hen. It wasn't fair on her. You need to be broad-minded. I mean, goodness knows what was going on in that nest-box.

Mrs Thomas, my neighbour, she looks after them when I'm not there. *She* understands.

Verity's late. Good grief! Over an hour, by that station-clock! Well, it's not the first time I've been left waiting on station platforms. Mind you, I'd never thought it of Verity...But it's him, obviously – *Christian*. He's afraid of what I might say. Men! They're all alike.

At least Andrew McAllister had the manners to keep in touch. He told me all the family news – let me know when each of the girls were born. And there was a standing invitation, if ever I wanted to go up to Edinburgh. But I didn't go, of course.

And then his wife, Crystal, left him. And now – he's passed as well.

Maybe I should go up to Edinburgh after all. I've got no ties – I'm fancy-free, as they say, and if you're needed, you always think of yourself last - .

The youngest – little Ellie – she'd only be about ten. Still needs a mother's care. After all, she doesn't know about men – *yet!*

12 IVY
The Fagg Street Trilogy
1 Meanwhile, Back in Fagg Street....

Norah? It's Norah Washbone, isn't it. I love supermarkets, don't you? I thought I saw you earlier, at the delicatessen counter. I shouted to you. Everyone heard me but you. I nearly got chucked out by that nice young security chap over there. You're not ignoring an old friend, surely...?.

Sorry for what...? Oh. Thought I was our Roxie, did you...?... Well, I've always known what you thought of her. But it's nice being mistaken for my own daughter. My Wally even says I remind him of a big movie star... Danny DeVito... Oh, it's only his sense of humour, Norah.

It must be years since me and you were neighbours in Fagg Street. Getting 'absent-minded' since you moved up to Parkfield Drive, are we...?

Beg pardon...? Oh, me and Wally – we're surviving. Course, *he's* still after that fortune he's hoping to win. He's wasted one already on the lotto and the geegees. And of course, I still go to Bingo at the Community Centre. That's why some of us are still stuck in Fagg Street.

So what have you and your Stan been up to, since he retired – stock-car racing? Bungie jumping...?

Ooh. Cheerful as ever – well, just like I might have expected. So with his hernia and prostate problems, there can't be much of him left, I suppose... oh, 'he's coping.' I'm glad to hear it. You just have to keep your pecker up, don't

77

Miss Iris Hoey as Zoie in
Baby Mine

you? Just like our Roxie, and look what she went through...
There now, you've just done it again... You always make such
a face if I so much as mention her name...

What d'you mean? Plunging neck-lines and mini-skirts up
to her boob-tube? Oh, that was just her way, our Roxie.
What they call 'creating her own style'. Like fire, she was.
Even when she was just a tiny tot, bless her. A real Jezebel.
And she still is. Remember when she had her eye on your lad
Gerald?

And on his father? Of course that's probably why your
Stan's the wreck he is today....

Our Roxie – she always needed a *real* man. Not a lot of hot
air and trousers - like Bert Clitheroe. On the night his fish-
and-chip shop got burnt down, he had to resign from the
Council. How's your Gerald getting on, by the way? I bet
you he's never looked at another woman since our Roxie...
Confused? Yes, that's just what we heard, back in Fagg Street.

Said his sexuality had been thrown into doubt? But with
those knickers he wore on the quiet, it always *was*. Same as
I said to Marge Eccles at Number Fourteen - and to some of
the others down at the Community Centre – where we serve
tea and cakes to the Evergreens, Tuesday and Friday
afternoon now, you know... Well, French boxer-shorts then!

With our Roxie having worked in Soho, she only wanted
to help, Norah. Give him a jolt *one* way or the other...

Right over the edge? Still has to go for counselling twice a
week? And he's on Prozac? Well, our Roxie always had the
best of intentions. Might have got a bit carried away maybe,
but at least your Gerald's landed up in safe hands.

Miss Dorothy Minto

Married now, you know... No. Our Roxie. He's a nice lad, Darren. Soft hands, but plenty of backbone. Mind you, he'd have to have, wouldn't he? But they've both settled down very well. And me and Wally – we're grandparents now. And proud of it...

Three. One of each. Always did things *her* way, eh...? It was only a joke, Norah. For goodness' sake, put a smile on your face. Life's a laugh! I mean where else would you put it?

And talking of laughs, Darren's just had a promotion. To Head Office. He's all for climbing up the ladder, is Darren. And him and our Roxie have just bought a new house. They're moving in, next week. Got great plans. 'Specially our Roxie. She's already been in touch with that programme *Grand Designs...* Oh, she won't be too far from you, love. Farnwood Road, just round the corner from Parkfield Drive...

2 *Pulling out the plug*

Norah? It's Norah Washbone, isn't it? A bit crowded in this café. Oh, you've got a coffee too, have you? I thought I saw you earlier, along the promenade. I shouted to you. Everyone heard but you. I nearly got accosted by that hunky young life-guard down there. Not ignoring an old friend, surely...? No, course not. Well, sit yourself down with your coffee. That's it, love. And let's have a chat. Just the two of us, girls together...

And is your Stan with you...? Oh, I always thought you both had your holidays in Spain or Portugal. Not here at Bog End-on-Sea... His prostate, was it...? Oh, I see – cholesterol. Well, he's certainly not the number one dog-trainer we knew when you both lived in Fagg Street. Though it must have been terrifying to work with those savage, man-eating beasts...

*Oh, right!...*Terrifying for the savage, man-eating beasts.

That move to Parkfield Drive didn't do either of you the slightest good, if you ask me...No, I'm only being *positive*, Norah. It's a gift, love. Even my Wally's the joker if he wants to be. Comes natural to us all in Fagg Street - being positive.

Take Elijah and Daisy Bates at Number Three. You'd never recognise them since our Roxie dropped in on them the other week... It's what she calls being 'community minded'. That's *all*, Norah. Something you and your Stan never were. Anyway, Elijah and Daisy are trying for another family now... that's right...With six grandchildren at the last count.

Got herself in with some research thing at the maternity unit, has Daisy. Goodness knows what chemicals they're pumping into her. And she must be all of sixty-nine...Oh, absolutely. I was surprised *he'd* got it in him... Like a ghost? He certainly looked like one after his first seizure. You should see him now he's on Viagra. Talk about Mister Grey Power! With everything screwed the right way on, thanks to our Roxie. Him and Daisy are selling their story to the *News of the World*. 'For an undisclosed sum,' so they said...

That's right, love. Well even my Wally couldn't crack a joke at that. I heard him say something about some people having all the flaming luck... Course you can't blame him really. He's lost a mint of money you know. Lives in that betting shop even on his holidays.

Which reminds me. I saw your lad Gerald on the beach, just now. And he'd actually taken his winter woolly off... goes surfing, eh? The girls'll be after him like sharks... Oh! Surfing the Internet. Not at that Cyber Café place...? Between Subway and Bargain Booze, on the High Street...? I thought it was only weirdos who get in there...

*Miss Sarah Brooke as Princess Gismonda and
Mr Lewis Waller as The Harlequin King*

Oh, still not himself? Well, who is he, then?

I don't think he's ever got over the time our Roxie took him to that heavy metal rock concert And those trainers had cost him ninety quid... Wrong, Norah. Her and her mates were only being 'community minded', like I said.

She's here at Bog End, by the way - teaching everyone how to enjoy life, as usual. Like me. She read this book, see. Called *Pulling out the Plug*. Roxie's planned all sorts of things to help us do it -relaxation and meditation, tonight, just for starters...

Oh, *sure*. There's a bit of line-dancing after. And then a moonlight swim. You and your Stan could come and join in the fun... He'd hyperventilate? Sounds like bad table-manners to me... Then just give him the chop. Least, for a couple of hours. This holiday's for your sake as well as his, isn't it? Go on. Be a devil.

'Take the bull by the horn!' as me and our Roxie would say... *Ole!* A moonlight swim? You really mean it? Honest? Oh, Norah. Then you're on...! Oh, don't worry. It's really private – the beach by our chalet.

D'you know love, I tried on my old swimming costume, last week? It's true. All doubled up, I was. Pulled down like Quasimodo by the neck halter... Well, that's right. You alter, don't you? 'Good grief, our mam! You won't need that thing,' our Roxie said. 'Not for skinny-dipping...'

Now... what's wrong with skinny-dipping, Norah? Got something to hide, have you – besides a bulging bank account...? *My* investments, they bulge in all the wrong places, but I don't care, nor does anyone else for that

Mr Henry Ainley as Faust

matter... So stop worrying... About your Stan and Gerald...? Oh, heck. Alright, then - all wimps welcome, *if* you insist. With a few cans of beer about the place, it'll be like a reunion – specially for our Roxie and your Gerald. *And* for his father...

No swimming-trunks? So what? If Stan's that fussy – how about those purple Y-Fronts of his? They'll be a sensation... What *about* the beach? Look, I told you. Of course it's private. One big private party. You'll meet all our Roxie's holiday friends. Nicos, Kosta and Theo – young Greeks mostly... And what's wrong with that? After all, they have joined the Common Market...

What about her husband? Oh... Darren? He took a tumble playing cricket, the other week. He just sits around, seeing to the kids, with his leg in plaster... Oh, Norah! 'Which *one?*' did you say? Your guess is as good as mine. But his team-mates have all signed it for him.

You'll be a new woman, Norah. Talk about *'Pulling out the Plug'*. After Elijah and Daisy Bates, it'll be you and your Stan for that maternity unit, thanks to our Roxie. You'll see...

What d'you mean, your Stan hasn't got it in him? Oh, hasn't he? Well, how do you think *I* know he wears purple Y-Fronts, Norah?

3 Fagg Street Floral Dance

Norah? Norah Washbone, isn't it? Pretty busy here at the Garden Centre, don't you think? I caught a glimpse of you earlier this afternoon, by the Venus Fly-traps. I shouted to you. Everyone heard me, but you. Not ignoring an old friend, surely?...

No, course not. I nearly got soaked to the skin by this young gardener, not looking where he was pointing his hose-pipe. He must have thought I was wilting, like the plants on your trolley, look... I can see you've got some real good bargains there. Stocking up that garden in Parkfield Drive, are we?

Where's your Stan by the way? It'd be nice to see him again... Oh, he's bound to have to keep going, the state of his waterworks. And your lad Gerald?... Stopped at home? What? On a day like today?... We know he had a 'nasty experience', love, but stamp-collecting's hardly the answer, is it?...

Well, it's a shame he doesn't get out more, shy or not. I'll tell you one thing - it's the quiet ones you have to watch – especially your Gerald! Some women really go for boyish looks like his. He's reminded me of Cliff for a long time... Cliff *Richard*, of course! I used to love Cliff Richard. In actual fact, I still think of him as *my* Living Doll. I do! Brings out the maternal instinct you see - just look at our Roxie, for instance. She always did her best to help your Gerald, when we were neighbours in Fagg Street... What d'you mean – 'Just made things worse'? That's gratitude, I must say!

She's just a girl who likes to know what's what, that's all.

Remember at Fiona Grant's twenty-first, was it her fault that the other girls, got him drunk on Vodka? She was the one who stopped him doing that strip-tease when he got down to his knickers... Sorry. French boxer-shorts.

And it was our Roxie who got him sent to that sexual therapist...Oh, he's still going? Well, it's obviously working, if he's started to read *Playboy*. I mean, given the right treatment, goodness knows what might come bursting out from under his winter woolly, or from that pair of hand-me-down flairs of his father's...

Our Roxie? Need you ask! Oh, she's here. Insisted on coming in her bikini, as it's so hot, this afternoon... Well, what else d'you expect? She's got that young gardener quite interested. The one I was telling you about. He keeps squirting water at her, instead of the herbaceous plants... Oh, of course she has, Norah. She's taken his name all right. And his mobile number... Report him? What for? Why, she's gone bananas over him. She's planning a hose party next week, giving him first refusal. The last I saw of them, he'd scored a direct hit in the agapanthus.

'Sides, we've all got good reason for a party. Wally, me and Roxie are on the telly shortly... To do with gardening – surprise, surprise! Yeah! In fact, it could end up being a street party. Like they had for the Coronation. I bet *you* can remember that, Norah.

It was during the 'fifties my mother – God bless the Good and Departed – actually shook hands with Percy Thrower – 'The Nation's Head Gardener'. Very excited, she was. And the same for our Roxie, the other week, when she met Alan Titchmarsh. And you know our Roxie, but I could see he

Miss Pauline Chase

was man-of-the-world enough to cope with the situation. Me and Wally met him, too… Oh, at the Gardens For All Show at the National Exhibition Centre, Birmingham - we went with Slaughter's Coaches.

It was a real achievement getting Wally away from that betting shop, I can tell you. And just like me and Roxie, he really enjoyed meeting all these celebrities.

Best of all though, was Clancy Redfall of Gargoyle TV… Oh, you've a soft spot for him too have you, Norah? Now there's a real gardener. A charmer, cheeky with the jokes, him and Roxie hit it off straight off. She even had a chat with his wife… You didn't know?… Of course, Astrid Venger, the famous film star. From Sweden. Just dropped by, on the way back to Hollywood for her next film.

And then Wally – of all people – who, for years, lost a fortune on the geegees, won the raffle! Top prize – a Garden Makeover!…You what, Norah? And what's wrong with our backyard?

'Something with strong, flowing lines,' suggested Clancy. 'With decking, and a water feature. And other things.…'

What d'you mean 'twee'? We can't all have Niagara Falls such as some I could name up in Parkfield Drive.

Anyway, our place, yesterday, was just like a building-site. And with those gorgeous hunks from Gargoyle TV Garden Busters, poor Roxie was beside herself! – with sound and camera crews thrown in for good measure.

Oh, things still happen in Fagg Street. Don't you think so, Norah? Sorry you and Stan ever moved to Parkfield Drive?… Be like that, then! But I could tell you one name

Miss Lily Brayton in Kismet

who was glad to get back from there. That was our Roxie. Least from Farnwood Road, just round the corner from you. Didn't suit her at all. Being community-minded, she tried all sorts of ways to get things going. Rave-ups, barbies, face-painting for the kids, Balti parties, psychic fayres...

'Stuck up' – that's what she said about the folk up there. They still preferred their flower arranging, whist drives, Tupperware parties and the 'golfing fraternity'. A bit different to the Garden Busters – up for anything, those lads. Put in a small lawn, they did, with a low shrub border and some conifers. Oh, and for privacy, some of that tall stuff that grows in clumps. Er - Bamboo! What pandas eat.

Clancy says when the wind blows, it'll make a sound like the rustle of spring. And d'you know, our Roxie's so impressed, she's going to write a poem about it... What d'you mean? Course she can write. Well – she knows her A's and B's, and that D comes after C. And she can watch her P's and Q's... So what, Norah? Like they say at Tescos: 'Every little helps.'

And she did just that on the programme... Helped the Garden Busters put in the decking - the latest craze, and she's got a 'thing' about decking. Then, d'you know, the statue for the water feature never turned up. Well, in no time it was Roxie to the rescue once more! A sensation when the show goes out, you'll see!

'Be architectural!' Clancy told her, when they plumbed her in. 'Something, let's say, between Queen Boadicia and the Statue of Liberty.' Looked great, she did – what with water coming out of her everywhere, and the children – April, Friday and even little Nolan – posed as cherubs. Everyone really enjoyed themselves, except Roxie's Darren - just 'cos he wasn't the centre of attention. Miserable beggar!

Then with the decking getting wet – another inspiration for our Roxie - an upbeat version of Titanic! Astrid Venger was really thrilled to bits about it. See, it only needs a word from her and our Roxie might even get asked to write the script. 'Hey, Mam!' she said, all excited this morning. 'What'd Norah and Stan Washbone think if I took their Gerald with me to Hollywood?'

It was then I told her how he reminded me of Cliff - or rather, Sir Cliff, as he is now. 'Cliff Richard?' she said, amazed. 'Dead ringer, our mam! With a part in the film, his hair bleached, and a workout with the weights, can't you see? Gerald could be the great new Leonardo diCaprio!

Well, Norah? What would you and your Stan think of that one, eh?

Mr Lewis Waller in Robin Hood

13 DULCIE
Have another one, Bunny

Dashed decent of you, Bunny, to come all this way to break it to your Aunt Dulcie. No, no, I'm all right, but you can help yourself, dear, over there in the corner. The little pink cocktail bar.

Your Commanding Officer, but your uncle too, dear, and I know how fond you were of each other. It must have been the most frightful shock for you. Shot, you say? By 'one of them'? A street skirmish in Delhi? Not the first time this month, according to the wireless. Humph! A skirmish? Not exactly a battle. But I'm sure he was as active as he could be, with that gammy leg.

Anyway, I don't suppose they have battles nowadays. At least, not the sort they'd have sent your Uncle Marcus to. A skirmish – sounds quite up to date, sort of thing. Mind you, he was bound to get bumped off sooner or later - there was a lot of your Uncle Marcus to shoot at.

Always a risk, Bunny, but you learn to live with the danger. You have to. I knew that right from the start. We all had to – the officers' wives - and their mistresses. And your uncle had heaps of *them*. At least, I hope he did, he deserved a little fun, poor boy.

Oh, don't look so shocked, Bunny. What are you, dear, thirty-five? I would have thought you'd have had a mistress or two yourself by now. Have another whisky, dear. It'll make you feel better.

*Miss Evelyn Millard as Lucy Allerton and Mr Lewis Waller
as Alexander Mackenzie in The Explorer*

Best way to go, Marcus always used to say. In action. Serving King and Country, God bless them. Britannia! The greatest mistress of all. On our coinage – on our paper money – true to form, she never looks you in the face. Always staring towards those countries that absolutely nobody's heard of, or even knows where they are, even in *this* day and age. I've heard it said that Mr Baldwin, our Prime Minister, actually takes forty winks - or more – during Cabinet meetings, when Foreign Affairs are mentioned. You'll have to excuse me, dear. Just the 'Little Woman' talking, as Marcus used to say. Not that he was putting me down, of course.

I simply hated those long postings abroad, Bunny. Especially in India. The gorgeousness of it so confused people, you see. There was such squalor, such terrible chronic poverty. People were dying on the streets from starvation, even amid all the pageantry and over-indulgence. And we were always travelling around in that heat. It does things to a man – and to a woman. Your Uncle Marcus wasn't the man he used to be, if you get my meaning, dear. That's really why I stayed at home all these years.

Actually, I suppose I was jolly lucky. So many of my school chums went abroad and stayed. They all married, of course. Some into the Army like me, some of them to tea planters, or to sweat it out on rubber plantations – or whatever they do on rubber plantations. It's the climate, dear , the boredom – *and* the loads of ghastly secrets that simply everyone knew about. Have another, Bunny – and have one for me.

Let me see, there was Hilda Clayton and Effie Woodrow – but I've got my reasons for not discussing them. Leonora Cato – 'Loopy Leonora', fifth daughter of the Earl of

Mr Lewis Waller in The Explorer

Colmore – such a queer family – she married Fifi Bridgett's eldest. What was his name now ? Ah, yes – Rupert! Twenty-third Lancers, if I remember. Wore a bearskin, would you believe. I think that was the trouble, in the end. She ran off with the yard boy. Went completely native.

Then there was little Kitty Curzon. Bled to death, poor thing, in some God-forsaken place. Africa. Something to do with childbirth, I think. And a witch-doctor. And Gertie Kane – the most marvellous dancer, trained with Isadora Duncan - it got to her all right. Took on religion, tore off all her clothes and danced in the altogether around this ancient idol in the Malayan jungle. Died completely batty, of course.

Oh, it's easy to be fooled by the tiaras, the presentation satins and feathers, Bunny. But the Colonel's Lady and Judy O'Grady – well, there's not a lot to choose between them. Canny old cove, that Kipling.

I've had more sense than most of them. Your uncle saw to that - he put me off men for good. And I don't think women are any kind of substitute, do you?

Brains will outlast beauty any day. I mean – look at *me*. I've entertained absolutely everybody – including the Prince of Wales. David used to love coming here, said it was so stimulating – until he got in with this Wallis Simpson. I told him the country would never accept an American Queen - I've not seen him since. But I'm sure he'll come to the Memorial Service. It'll be full military honours for your uncle, and the Abbey. 'Simply spiffing, old thing!' Marcus would have said.

Let's have another drink, Bunny. Why, dear, whatever are you doing on the floor?

Miss Lily Elsie as Alice in The Dollar Princess

14 CINDERELLA
Miss Lonelyheart

Miss Zelda, can you hear me? No? Oh, this damn' mobile phone! I'll never get the hang of it! Hello – yes! Right! So...

'Seems like forever I stand,
Hand on hip,
In my black stockings, Doc Martens,
Leathers – plus whip.'

Now, are you going to put that in Saturday's edition or not?......Why not?.........

Hello, hello!... Miss Zelda?....You still there?

Oh, damn.... damn this phone!... Hello?....

Oh, you are? Good....Well, I repeat – why not?

It's Cinderella Walklate, if you remember, Miss Zelda. The girl who hates housework....I am desperate...

But why? What d'you mean – not original? So what? It was put in last week – by someone else...

Put people off? Well I hope he/she/it got nil response! – No, I'm not being catty....

Huh – all this business of 'Ring 0800 whatever, and have your personal number tally with others on our *Meet That Someone Special* computer – the famous Miss Zelda LaTouche advising you on Perfect Partnerships'...

Why don't I go back to *Olive Oyl Seeks Popeye?*..

Oh, sure! More of *Sleazy Charmer*, I suppose, *Twin-Track Initiative*, *Light My Fire*, *Home Alone* – and Cecil, who liked watching *Neighbours* repeats and racing snails! ... Not to mention Bixie, who looked like a Cuban mercenary, in her flacks and lead-lined boots. *And* she shaved!

A day when the computer got its genders mixed up? Seems like it wasn't the only one...

No, no excuses, it's a poor workman who blames his tools, Miss Zelda, if you don't mind my saying.

I'm too fussy?... *Game For A Laugh?*..

Well, okay, maybe I've got a sense of humour. But it's a contract for life we're talking about, Miss Zelda...

Who's old-fashioned?...Then so's a million others.

That two-page spread – your Personal Column – now it's barely one. I reckon *Saturday Night is the Loneliest Night of the Week*, as the song goes. But every night's the loneliest for some....

Who's feeling sorry for themselves? Certainly not me!

What d'you mean 'What do I mean?'...

Me with my duster and Pledge, and my two ugly sisters gorging themselves silly on chocolate oranges, we used to regularly watch Sammy Icon's – now *there's* a case – his *Midnight Show* on the telly.

Zelda LaTouche, great ex-movie star! The way you matched up couples over the phone, chosen at random from the studio audience. Now that was terrific!! Okay, some said that it was a con – but they all got married, didn't they?

101

Everyone was itching to see you again – like me. God! We all thought you were dead!..

Then hey - Miss Zelda LaTouche! *Garbo of the Blind Date* – now working on our local paper!

BUT!!! Don't think I don't know about you – and that two-page spread now being one page...

Never ever talk to me in such a tone of voice, Miss Zelda! Saturday night and my ad goes in – d'you hear? Else all sorts of chaotic numbers'll keep coming up. *Frog Princes* etc for all...'Cos I've seen enough deadbeats, Miss Zelda, it's over and out for Cinderella Walklate from here on. I've got my real prince, and I'm having a ball!

So don't you keep phoning *me* each day, every day. Try Sammy Icon, with his problems – those Versace gowns, and *Tales of Mother...*

He doesn't fit? Doesn't...Doesn't fit what?... Now, now – don't get over-heated, Miss Zelda.. ...You're old? Why, everyone knows that...

...But me, *I* fit? *I fit the profile??? Me?*

....They want me? *They want me to be Zelda II???*

...Oh, no thanks, there's some mistake somewhere!

Hello! Hello!...WOW!..Hey, she's blown! .... WOW!! Miss Zelda? – You alright, Miss Zelda?...Oh, God!..

...um....six-four...damn...three-two-zero....

...extension seven-three five... .....quick! Is that Computer Maintenance?

Miss Alexandra Carlisle

15 RUBY
Down on the Farm

The hole in that hedge gets smaller, every week. I've told Baxter the sooner he gets busy with his badging-hook the better, up here in Nettle Meadow. I wouldn't dream of telling you where I've just had a lump of hawthorn stuck.

Baxter Wildblood's my sweetheart, you know. We've had a secret life for over forty years, and he's been foreman here at Barcroft Farm for near thirty-five of them. As a lad, he joined the Army, lusting for adventure. He's always enjoyed taking risks - like going again yesterday to see the woman who's been his wife for thirty-five years. Doreen Camellia - she only lives a couple of miles into town, so he should've been back by now. This time though, he says it's the final break-up. He says that every time, and what I want to know is - the final break-up of what?

Well, whatever hold she's got over him, I know that Baxter does love his belly. And him and me – we've enjoyed many a harvest supper of mine, even before he went into the Army. Look! I always pack his ham sandwiches, straight off the bone. It's his favourite, for if he shows up here today. With a bit of jam roly-poly on the side. And we've both had plenty of that, specially of a Friday lunch-time like now, up here in the wide blue yonder.

He's so romantic, is Baxter. 'My big, red Ruby,' he calls me. And he's right, cos there's a lot of me, and I'm worth plenty – in the right setting!

He's got these old-fashioned ways. When he raises his cap,

Miss Hutin Britton and Mr Matheson Lang

his bald head steaming, there's many a door he's opened to let me in. He's just what any woman would want when she's got a husband like my Eli, who sits on his tractor all hours, or else is acting chief herdsman, head ploughman or number one haymaker, with our three strapping lads giving him a hand while the sun shines.

Meantime, Baxter and me, we've made stacks – 'on manoeuvres'. Though I couldn't believe it one day, when husband Eli told me he'd got the urge. 'What's brought this on?' I asked him.

'Weather,' he said, pulling on his Wellies. 'But I s'pose I'd best go and spray the mangold-wurzels, instead.'

Now Baxter I could always rely on for his goings and his comings. Even my old dad – years ago – looked up to him. 'Why don't you marry this fine young soldier-boy!' he'd ask, lying pie-eyed on his back in the Snug, with Baxter standing over him, saluting Queen and Country.

When Dad cocked his toes, Baxter was like a father and a husband standing in the same pair of socks. He said they were days of 'necessary economy'. Well, he's what you'd call 'educated' is Baxter. He's learned me a thing or two between times. He knew about women, you see. Off soldiering in foreign parts, he met all the beauties of the World. Like Miss Francaise, Miss Italy, Miss Ceylon, Miss Peru. He could charm the lot at those Top Brass army do's – all of them queuing for a bit of a jig with Baxter.

Now you'd have thought I'd have been jealous, wouldn't you? Well, not a bit of it – 'cos it was my parts he always came back to, like any good soldier, preferring the territory he knew best. He tried to warn me about my reputation once, but it didn't matter, really. We've all got reputations round here, even the Reverend Smarty, who often pops his head round kitchen door for a taste of my steaming hot-pot.

It was him who married me and Eli. We go back to ever - as far as Baxter, nearly.

I was seventeen when I went the first time to the Conservative Young Farmers' social at the village hall. Baxter was off on duty in Cyprus, and he didn't mind me going on my own, though he did tell me not to mix politics with romance. But I couldn't help myself. A hot night, the men were dancing in their shirt-sleeves. And through the crowd, I saw this handsome young chap, sitting all on his own at the bar – in a suit! Now I've always had a thing about expensive suits. I went straight over.

At first, he kept looking at his watch, then we started chatting all about money mostly – his. And he said he thought me a worthwhile investment, so he bought me a triple cider. He did. Talk about a whirlwind romance? Next thing, me and Eli had set the date, cos he'd got to be back at the farm within the hour.

Then soon after that, I heard Baxter Wildblood had eloped with his sergeant major's daughter, Doreen Camellia. But it didn't last. The Doreen part of her was bossy, he said, and the Camellia bit was 'too refined'. And anyway, he'd missed my wholesome apple dumplings – and more wholesome things besides. After five years in the Army, he was back. For good.

'I'm in need of a reliable man on the farm,' Eli told him. 'A man I can trust. With the livestock.' I wondered if he meant me. Baxter, saluting, got set on there and then. But he'd nip off now and again, to see his 'stranged wife. And believe me, she was strange, cos he'd come back in a bad mood – and always frowning. He said she'd said she'd find him somewhere decent to work if he fancied going back to her. The nerve! And he said he'd be happier standing up to his knees in cow muck. But Doreen Camellia – she's still dangling her carrot.

After we married, Eli said he loved me just once, when he had the time. That meant a lot to me, even though he puts me second to his herd of Friesians and when his prize pigs farrow, he'd sooner spend the night with an old sow than with me. But I'll tell you one thing - if my old dad was alive today, he'd be dead chuffed to know who the real father of my three strapping lads is!

Well! Carrot or no carrot, here's my man right now! And he's not frowning, he's waving, Nettle Meadow all of a tremble – like me. Not quite the spring chicken he was, but like it says on a bag of garden peat, he's still 'all that Nature intended.' Ham sandwiches straight off the bone, today. And plenty of bacon and crackling from tomorrow on, eh Baxter!!!

16 PEGGY-LOU
Sundown Sweetheart

Howdy, friends it's me in person. Little old Peggy-Lou, the one-time Number One Country Western Singer you all know from guest appearances and hit records of not so long ago.

I was raised on Happy Homestead Farm, Bunnyhug Hill, Nashville, Tennessee. We was all real close – my Mammy and Pappy, my sister Ruby Belle and me, and my brothers Gus, Buck and Baby Blue.

After I graduated from High School, me and my brother Buck, we got an act going as the Blue Grass Rockabillies. Oh, we was just young and hopeful, but we got asked to take our geetars everywhere – church halls, barn dances, and the local radio stations. And we sure made them sit up, Buck and me. Got to be the talk of the county and things were looking good for us.

Then Buck, he chickened out and skedaddled back home to the farm. Got himself hitched. Looking back, maybe he was the one saw sense.

But me, I still kept on trying – going solo as Peggy-Lou. And in the end, I struck the big time. Came second in a nation-wide country singers' competition on radio, and got myself signed up by Tim T. Wibble of ABD Records. He said my raunchy style was 'sure fire unique'. Yessiree, Bobtail!

Then came the sunshine years of fame – but I was always

Miss Gertie Millar as Kitty Kent in
The Marriage Market

hitting that road. Travelled the States – and Europe. I had a great following in that little old United Kingdom. Yet all the time, I couldn't help thinking about the folks back home, which in a way, brought a tear or two to my style of singing. And that was no bad thing.

I filled that little old Carnegie Hall. I brought style and rhythm to the Ed Sullivan Show in my own special sort of way. But in spite of it all, I couldn't help feeling that something was missing. Seemed like in spite of all the fame, I was walking nothing but a long, lonesome road.

And I wasn't the only one to feel that way. Nights when we sat around the camp fire, passing the apple-jack, some of us, we'd get to talking things over. Johnny Denver, Glenn Campbell, Slim Whitman, Kenny Rogers, Dottie West, Dolly Parton and me. And there was others, some now departed to the sound of distant drums beating in that old Injun sunshine over them legendary Black Hills of Dakota. Yessiree – there was good times – and there was bad.

Even my agent, a dumb city slicker, don't speak to me no more. I gave him a ring the other day, just the same.

'Hi, Rory,' I said.

'Why hi there, Bobby Jo,' he came back.

'It ain't Bobby Jo,' I told him. 'It's doggone Peggy-Lou.'

'Who?' he puzzled. I could just see him in my mind, scratching that old shaved head of his.

'Peggy-Lou, and I'm doggone tired of wandering the country roads like some geetar-tooting lonesome lovesick hobo!'

111

'Oh, hi Peggy-Lou,' he said, not a spark of welcome, his voice as dry as tumbleweeds. 'What can I do for you?'

'Jest do your job proper and git me some good gigs like that old Carnegie Hall again. I'm on hard times, Rory,' I said, trying not to sound too pleading. 'I still sing with sunshine in my heart.'

'Sure thing, Peggy-Lou, but like you said yourself, you're just lovesick. It ain't no Carnegie Hall you want – it's a Dating Agency.'

Now that got me to thinking. That was when I recollected how Rory was born near the Blue Ridge Mountain River, so he ain't so dumb after all.

Some folks just live on memories. Embers of love. But me, I ain't even put match to paper! Well, that ain't strictly true, cos when I was a little girl, I teased, I flirted with country boys by the score. But I guess I never really took love on board – not the real thing. And like the song goes, if you ain't loving, you ain't living!

I used to reckon on how love would be an interference in my life. Wal, it sure is – but it's the not having any that's the problem with me right now. Maybe I've been a-waiting all these years for my beau to come spitting and chewing down from the High Country. He'll be getting a bit long in the tooth by now – but that's okay with me so long as the Good Lord has spared him his own. I'll put up with the bow legs.

I reckon he'll spread his horse blanket on the ground for us to lie together, with them coyotes hollering at that old full moon the whole night through. Though when you get to my age, you kind of prefer Grandma's Feather Bed.

Come the morning, maybe we'll board that Orange Blossom Special and go rooting tooting off down the line. Destination? Where the rainbow ends.

So, hi guys! If you've liked what you've seen here on Cutie Cupid's Dating Agency website, maybe you'll give me a call. Huh? I'll be waiting – and hoping!

17 RHODA
Lady Musketeers

I've delivered them all. Big baby boys, small baby boys. And most of them stay that way all their lives. Just baby boys.

I remember the first confinement I attended on my own. Janice Piper. She was only eighteen. The doctor'd been delayed, and I was brandishing the forceps and yelling at her to give me something to catch hold of. And she was yelling at me to shut up and leave her alone, because she was going to die anyway. Then all of a sudden, out it came like a young eel. A big baby boy.

Angie, one of my best mates, actually married one, as well as training as a qualified State Nurse. She had to work all hours. Then one day, she said to me 'Rhoda, he can't take it!' Just what you might have expected – and not long after, he threw a tantrum at being a 'house husband', and cleared out. Good riddance, I said.

My other best mate, Bev, only had to shoot them a look with those deep green eyes of hers if they ever thought about trying anything on. She'd say she was into Thai Kick-boxing (although she'd only had a couple of lessons) and they'd just dissolve. But she could kick where it hurts most, all right.

I can hardly remember my Dad. Played football in his spare time apparently, and some of the older folk still talk about the goals he scored. He died in the Merchant Navy, in the war. And Mum, 'doing her bit', took in gentlemen lodgers. Huh – them I could handle. Just big baby boys.

Miss Pauline Chase

...But there was him, he was different - Uncle Leo, I called him. He came as foreman at the local market garden. Good to have him around – and he was, for a long time. Smelled of the outdoors, and padded about like a huge, friendly bear. Nothing subtle about him. He'd exchange smiles with Mum when he slipped her an extra turnip, or even a bottle of scent or a box of chocolates. Black market, obviously.

But then, he started to smile at me, different. Specially when I got older. And there was once when ... he went ... further. Or at least, I thought he did....

Him – the sort, let's say, best not talked about, not even to your closest friends – like Angie and Bev.

There's not a lot we don't talk about. Been there, seen it, done it. We're all midwives now. As student nurses, we lived in the hostel near the old Surgical Block. When we had time off together, we used to doll up, pile into Angie's Mini – all of us big girls, even then – and roll into town for a great night out at the Palais or the Trocadero. We went there for years, 'till the Palais got knocked down for road-widening, and the Trocadero turned to Bingo.

Angie's Mum used to call us the 'Lady Musketeers', Angie, Bev and me. We liked that at the time. 'All for one - and one for all!' – though we never shared a bloke. Angie liked hers skinny, with brains, while Bev fancied plenty of beefsteak, well grilled. And me, well ....

Course a lot of questions always got asked. Not that we actually heard them, mind. But you could read them on people's faces whenever the three of us walked in and cleared the floor. Like – where were the men in our lives?

Miss Marie Lohr

By then, Angie had got shot of that husband of hers for permanent– he hadn't been skinny and he hadn't had brains. That was probably the trouble. And Bev, somehow she was still foot-loose and fancy free.

But there was this Gavin, that fancied me. A persistent little bloke, about forty – lecturer, so he claimed, at the Outward Bound School, all toughness and self-reliance. He kept showing up all the time, any old time, even when I was on duty. Toughness? He saw me take a blood sample from somebody's arm and threw up on the spot. That took care of him.

It can get a bit lonely in this flat sometimes, I must admit. It would be really nice to have someone you liked to cook for, sit down to a meal with....He worked six days a week at the market garden, but he had his dinner most Sundays with Mum and me ...And he always brought me some little thing...

But on my seventeenth birthday, he gave me this record - my very first record. Bill Haley and the Comets. *Rock around the Clock*. And we played it, him and me, while Mum was in the kitchen, doing the dishes.

He said he was going to teach me to do Rock 'n' Roll. But I just couldn't seem to get the hang of it. We tried and tried. He was really patient with me. We laughed and laughed, that afternoon. And in the end, he gave me a great big hug... Two weeks later, he left.

I never did get the hang of Rock 'n' Roll...

Lounging round in front of the telly, Sunday papers and a big box of soft centres – that sort of scene – well, it's not much fun on your own. On the other hand, we're never stuck for company, Angie, Bev and me. We only have to give a buzz on the mobile to one or the other – or both. 'Cos the three of us all live close.

But we do still like to keep our eyes open for any comers – though they don't seem to come so much, these days.

Tomorrow, it's Singles Night at Shabby Abbie's. Live entertainment, the music – it's great, so they say. We thought we'd give it a try. Though I expect they'll be the usual kids, shave once a fortnight. Baby boys. Scared I might grab them by the forceps a second time????…

Miss Mabel Love

18 VENUS
A Love Goddess Reflects

I took a look at myself through the looking-glass this morning. I couldn't say who turned away the quickest – me or the looking-glass, I told my old Dad, Jupiter.

'That's a fine thing to say,' he boomed at me, 'considering that you're Venus, the Goddess of Sexual Love and Beauty.'

'But have you had a look at me lately? No – you haven't. Well?' I said. So he pushed his long white hair out of his eyes.

'Good grief!'

'That's what I mean,' I said. 'Neither fat nor thin. Just sagging!'

'Like an old mattress,' he agreed.

Hardly the voluptuous creature I once was. Well, I had to face it. Gone were the days when I could attract the likes of Mars or Adonis – brainless, that boy, but beautiful. I said to Jupiter: 'I don't feel like a goddess at all. Sexual Love and Beauty – pull the other one!'

He was quite put out and reminded me that I was the Goddess of Gardens as well, and that a Roman emperor dedicated a garden to me on the Via Sacra. Yes – and I had to do all the digging and planting for it! Oooooh! I've never been the same since.

'Only figuratively speaking,' Jupiter shouted.

'I don't care,' I shouted back. 'I'm giving in my notice. I'm going to retire and eat myself into a big fat momma.'

Well, perhaps I wouldn't have gone that far, but he nearly collapsed when I said it! You see, as the Goddess of Sexual Love and Beauty, I used to be really on top of the job. My reputation, my figure – all of them, gods, goddesses, mortals, the lot – they were just dazzled. I had my pick – and I didn't stint myself. When I was Aphrodite all those years ago, I had the King of Troy after me. Quality, that's always been my trademark.

It was what they call a conflict of interests that forced me to think about retiring. We can all have them. Diana, the Goddess of Hunting, now – one minute chasing animals in the forest with a bow in her hand, the next minute expected to lead petitions defending their rights. Didn't know where she was. *And* the Goddess of Virginity too – but as I'm sure you can well imagine, that's yet another story - !

The best job in the world. That was what everyone said I'd got. Fair enough, when I was Aphrodite. But if I was to make a celestial appearance now – to some innocent boy scout, say – he'd grab his rucksack and run for it.

The trouble is, I'm not so young as I was. Those Roman soldiers, they had a lot to answer for when they went marching home, leaving us all behind, Diana and me and my old man Jupiter and the rest. I'm not so badly off in my place, it's detached and quite comfortable – on the well-off side of town. But Diana's stuck in the woods of course, and she finds that the cold winters and the damp don't do her rheumatism any good at all. She's had to call it a day as far as the hunting is concerned, too, but she's taken up

Mr Basil Gill as Caesar in Antony and Cleopatra

voluntary work at the Animal Lifeline shop. She's always been around animals, so she enjoys it – and they've got three fan heaters!

And now I think about it, those Romans weren't so bad. If we'd all trooped back with them to the shrines in Italy, who would have been here now, doing my job for instance?

I am the Goddess of Love, and that's something that matters. Who would be taking care of love if I wasn't here? If there were just words carved on some weathered tablet of rock, for instance? Words like love – desire – passion - ?

Not that anybody really knows what they mean anyway. But they are – as the saying goes – what makes the world go round. And I suppose I understand them better than most.

I didn't ask to be the Goddess of Love, but I've been doing it for a long time. And, sagging or no sagging, it's me they all turn to. Because there's something else about love. It's blind. So when people look at me, I suppose they just see – Venus. Know what I mean?

19 ELLEN
Mrs Shepley

'Oh, Mummy, Mummy, what shall I do?' I pleaded. 'Please don't die!'

'Nonsense!' she wheezed, fighting manfully against the morphine injection. 'Mummy's got to die so that you, my darling Ellen, can live!'

That was only six months ago and now – how things have changed. This is the greatest day of my life. Waiting here at the Savoy in my wedding dress for the white Rolls Royce. I think I *must* have lived. I don't know what I've done to deserve it.

I hardly knew what to do when Mummy passed on. So I let him – Mr Shepley, my pen-friend of many years – know immediately. We had met on several occasions in London, and I knew I could rely on him. When he arrived, everyone said how fortunate I was to have him to lean on. And, goodness me, how right they were. I'd always been used to Daddy being around, in the past.

It was shortly after Mummy and Daddy came back from India that I was born. Daddy settled into being 'something' in Whitehall – there for many years – very hush-hush – in order to see Mummy very comfortably off. And when Daddy passed on, of course Mummy couldn't cope alone, so I had to keep tabs on the family investments. But in spite of taking the *Financial Times*, I was never very good at it.

Mummy had warned me of certain scoundrels who

Miss Alice B. Crawford

*Mr Gerald du Maurier as Le Duc de Charmerace
in Arsène Lupin*

targeted women for their money – 'having their way in more ways than one'! Mummy's own words. She could be very *avant garde* at times.

In fact, Mr Shepley told me he'd known several such men! So him being an expert in all sorts of investments, I felt safe in putting all my assets into his capable hands. At first he wouldn't hear of it, saying my own financial acumen was quite remarkable. But I insisted. 'Better to be safe than sorry!' as Mummy and Daddy would have said.

They both used to call me 'The Jewel of their Advancing Years.' And in a way, I suppose I was. Changing the beds, washing, ironing, cooking – keeping the entire house as bright as a button. And as for gardening…! Even though I did my best, it was never up to Daddy's rigorous standards.

It was Daddy who introduced us, years ago – Mr Shepley and I. Not used to meeting men – especially such handsome, prosperous ones – I blushed and blushed. Silly *me!*

Daddy knew him at the Club, so that proved he was all right. Debonair, so full of *joie-de-vivre;* tall enough to push back the clouds, and such a firm handshake! His job took him all over the world, and oh, it all seemed too, too glamorous! Our actually corresponding about our common interest – the Theatre! I absolutely adore the Theatre. Not on the stage, Heaven forbid! - I'd forget my words, bump into the furniture, and feel such a fool.

But Mr Shepley whisked me into the West End whenever he could – which wasn't very often, because of his job. Twice, actually, when I was able to leave Mummy for a few hours.

Of course, I'm not what you'd call pretty. Quite plain,

actually – like Jane Austen. My Cousin Audrey was the one! Secretly entering a competition at work – ending up as 'Blazing Batteries' Beauty Queen'! Caused a furore in the family, the photographs and all the publicity. 'Good for her!' I thought, though I never dared to actually say it.

But even though I'll never be a Beauty Queen, Mr Shepley says I'm his shining jewel. His little diamond dove. It's my inner qualities, he's always telling me, that count. Like a diamond – he says I'm quite transparent.

Mr Shepley, of course, has always been a man of many parts – including being married. I told him I didn't want to know anything about his past. Called *trust*, you see. But he insisted. He confessed he had been married twice, and had terrible problems with women. It was so unfortunate, his wives not understanding him. Yet I understand him perfectly, without even trying. He says ours is the perfect rapport, after all his years of trouble.

All the same, remembering Mummy's words, I had to be sure.

'I've never seen your name among the money moguls in the *Financial Times*', I ventured.

'Nonsense darling,' he replied, his wide blue eyes twinkling. 'It's there every day. Invisible earnings.'

Well, I've never seen it,' I said.

'Exactly. Don't worry your pretty little head about such matters ever again,' he laughed, throwing back his head of thick, greying hair. Such a sense of humour! I felt so reassured. The relief! No more household bills to pay! In fact, no more household! It went for a very good price – and the garden – Mr Shepley saw to that.

Taking hold of both my hands, he swore they would never again be soiled by housework, and he slipped his mother's ring onto *this* finger. See – a garnet. It's of such sentimental value to him. And he's promised me that where I am going, I will never have to even lift a finger. But he's insisted on it being a surprise.

So our wedding day has been a sort of elopement. Just the two of us going to the Register Office. Of course, I didn't expect a fuss for his *third* marriage. But I'd reckoned without Mr Shepley's sensitive nature. He *insisted* on the white dress. After all, as he knows better than anyone, I can wear white with a *clear conscience*. Mr Shepley respected me so much he was prepared to wait – but he says that after we're married, he'll get everything he's always wanted from the new Mrs Shepley.

It's quite overwhelming! - the big moment at last! *Just like a Grimms fairy-tale* - placing my life into my darling's strong, capable hands!!!!

20 CARLA
Oscars Night with the Stars

Back in the limelight, seems kinda strange being short on words, standing up here tonight, in front of all you lovely people--. I am a very, very private person, I guess. I always have been a very private person.

But I cannot let this moment pass without saying, to each and every one of you – thanks, and thanks again for this wonderful honour. I just love you all. I want to thank you all – and I want to thank especially my late Momma, Emmy, for having me, between Thanksgiving and New Year in that old, beat-up shack – and who shouldn't have!

See, I never knew my father. I don't reckon Momma did, either. Momma was a very, very private person too.

I want to give a very big thank-you to Pastor Ricky Mendoza, that chubby guy who saved me when I was just a li'l downtown gal. Pastor Ricky, he kept telling me that: 'Narrow is the Path of Righteousness', and he just devoted himself to keeping me on that path. He just lived for my soul ... till I got myself voted 'Miss California Orange' in a talent contest. Then, I guess, the path wasn't wide enough for the both of us.

That was in 1954. And then came my screen test, my cheque for two thousand dollars – and all those movies! And Mr California Orange – Huck Thompson. Muscles that kinda rippled like waves ...er ...like waves ...on the Sargasso Sea. Tall and tanned, greased dark hair swept back, that was Huck. The press were all ready to have the pair of us hitched – and I was just struck dumb by that fast automobile of his. Sleek Austin Atlantic, with white-walled tyres. I kinda loved white-walled tyres. Trouble was, so did Huck. Why, that dumb cluck was more married to that automobile than he ever could be to me.

I want to pay a special tribute to my late personal analyst, Dr Klaus Klinkel. It was Dr Klinkel who made me the woman I am today. He told me to be positive – that I was a very positive kinda person. It was Dr Klinkel who kept me going through those years when there were no movie-parts on offer. They were awful hard...

But he kept right on telling me I was a positive kinda person. And I kept right on telling myself I was a positive kinda person. Awful shame 'bout poor old Klaus – who'd just lived for my brain.... He was the one got screwed up in the end, I guess. I mean, he just must have been screwed up to jump from the sixty-seventh floor....

I want to give an extra big thank you to the director of all my early movies, John Blizenheimer III – 'Blitzie' - . The man who kinda didn't forget me those couple years back, when he was casting Old Martha in *The Sad Father of Farewell Tom.*

I just loved Old Martha. I guess everybody loved Old Martha – that supergran of eighty-seven, six facelifts, five husbands, and having it off with that neat college professor with an identity problem - ! Gee! I was shedding tears for Old Martha the very first time I read the script. That sad, wonderful story that had the whole of America shedding tears – all of us eatin' popcorn and shedding tears together. United States in the true sense of the word!

I guess I just mustn't forget to thank my co-director, John Blizenheimer IV – son of John III. It was Johnnie who took over on the sudden demise of his old father – 'Blitzie' – after we'd had those few private moments together….'cos we were both very private people, you understand - .

Johnnie, as you know, isn't able to be here with us tonight, either. He takes his responsibilities as my co-director very seriously, and after him and me took a look in at the Casino earlier on today – well, I was kinda fine, but Johnnie, he didn't feel so good. Shot himself in the foot – didn't make a very good job of it at all - ! But if you're watching from that bed of pain, Johnnie, don't you worry about a thing. I'm organising a whip-round among these lovely, lovely people. Dig deep, folks, for a really great guy!

Like Old Martha, you know, I can still give the men a run for their money – 'specially if they've plenty of it. I mean, I jump rope and pump iron for four hours every day – thanks to my wonderful trainer, Randy Exton….

Randy, he just lives for my body. And he's fine – for the moment. I reckon as how that is the real secret of life – just living for the moment. Like this wonderful, wonderful moment – standing here holding this wonderful, wonderful Trophy….

I feel so highly honoured to accept this long-deserved award. This is a very deep and private moment for me. A private moment I want to share now with you all, through radio, TV, cable and satellite – both in here and way out there in the big, big world, the Universe and Beyond….

To each and every one of you, thank-you. I love you all….

Miss Neilson-Terry

21 ANGELA
The Last Dance

'Beam me down, Scottie!' I said jokingly, in my 'Star-ship Enterprise' frame of mind.

'Beam yourself down!'

That was the boss, Archangel Gabriel, who pushed this PC into my hand. So – *voila!* Angel 426, in Earth Mode. Mission – to 'earn my wings', as they say in the RAF, after so long an apprenticeship. And to earn myself a name.

You couldn't mistake Piggie's name - Piggie Gillespie, at 2am fast asleep here in his Emperor-sized bed with his wife – his second wife – Beattie. His squashed features are rather similar to a Vietnamese pig, aren't they? Complete with pot belly, too. And – if he only knew it – ready for the 'Big Off', eh, Piggie?

Remember Angela from years ago? – your *first* wife? Angela of the egg-cup league, poor soul? Nothing to do with football. Although looking at Beattie, she's got two. Implants, obviously. And showing as much cleavage as immodesty allows.

Not like I used to be, am I? Oh, they make you into a tough cookie up there in Heaven – those survivors' courses for new arrivals who've been abused, you see. Aha! Now you turn away! Go on, snore as much as you like! But you'll hear me via your conscience, just the same.

You realise I do have a name after all? That young woman who, besotted, loved you because she could see what you *could* be? Me, yes, me – Angela herself, whose world was scholarly enterprise, eye strain and poetry.

Men never make passes
At girls who wear glasses.

But you did, Piggie. You were the only one. After that night at the Town Hall dance, when some school friends dared me to go up on stage, and do a song with your band. There you were, podgily seated at the piano, resplendent in your ill-fitting black trousers, red sequinned jacket and crocodile grin. And then our first dance together. Magical. I simply had to tell *everyone* about you.

I always had the feeling I'd die young. So why did I marry you? If you really want to know, it was because I was bursting with wild, undisciplined love and admiration for you, of course. You with no parents or family – just Piggie, who'd had to fight every step of the way to where he'd got – or that's what he said.

It was like a thrilling film. There were famous bandleaders of the day - Geraldo, Victor Silvester, Edmundo Ross - all praising this boy from the back streets for his innovative style. And you, boasting of the offers, contracts, opportunities, lying at your feet. You were terrific! A real hero!

I'd always imagined dying of some romantic fatal illness. Rather like *The Lady of the Camellias*. But you were more down to earth, Piggie. Wrestling – not with angels – but with an awesome truth that my wild love and admiration had hidden from me. But had revealed – oh, so much more clearly to you.

So – I became part of the earth – my mortal remains, that is. Courtesy of the perfect crime. Congratulations, Piggie. I never knew you had it in you. Apart, that is, from your motto: '*Me and my mouth:* we make a great team together.'

Oh, it wasn't my admiration you couldn't cope with, Piggie. It was my blind, overwhelming love. But after you killed me, you were no better off. I'd obviously wanted you to be what you *couldn't* be. I can see that now.

Beattie Boobs, on the other hand, has got more sense. She readily accepts you for what you are. Just a small-town musician by night, foreman in greasy overalls at the garage down the road, by day. Sorry – Manager now, so I hear. Again – congratulations! But – it's the same old bull and bluster: living in a Never-Never Land of TV appearances, hype and recording contracts always almost to hand – never quite materialising.

The night is running out. It's time for the 'Big Off'. Your day of reckoning is dawning, Piggie. No – snoring won't help you now, nothing will. Only I could help you, if I wanted to. And why would I want to? Believe me, I've waited a long time to have my revenge.

But – would revenge earn me my angel's wings? Would vengeance lift me – and would I want it to? Might things finally go right for you if you had another chance, Piggie? Perhaps I'll never know. But – I'm going to beam myself back to where I came from now, okay? On my own.

Maybe you will never make it. But, tell you what, Piggie. Whether I've earned my wings or not, I'll save the last dance – for old times' sake – just in case.

A SHORT HISTORY OF THEATRICAL POSTCARDS
by Alicia Crow

You can trace the whole development of entertainment in the late 19th and the 20th century in postcards, along with almost every other topic you can think of. The postal card was first introduced in 1869 in Austria, but it was the Paris Exhibition of 1889 that really marked the beginning of the craze for sending and collecting them.

Illustrated colour cards were produced in their millions, and by the end of the 19th century there was a thriving industry producing all kinds of cards and the albums collectors demanded to store and display their collections. Many of the oldest were 'black and white' or sepia toned, and for a coloured effect they were tinted by hand. The results could be lovely.

Though intended to be sent through the mail to 'keep people in touch' the early postcards were often small works of art. Among the most popular were the holiday postcard, the 'wish you were here' kind of view sent to family and friends of seaside resorts, beautiful scenery or historic landmarks. Increasingly, however, portraits of the famous – whether in the spheres of politics or entertainment, sport or just 'in the news' – began to interest the general public, who often collected many different photographic cards of their favourites.

Postcard and Memorabilia Fairs prove fascinating haunts for railway, military, motoring or general topographical cards, and there are rich pickings to be found today – often unexpectedly – in junk and second-hand shops, car-boots and street market stalls. Thanks to the Antiques Road Show and similar TV programmes, few people today are likely to throw out the contents of Great-Grandma's attic as 'just junk', for we are well aware that there could be potential gold nuggets hidden among those dusty boxes of papers and personal trivia.

From the theatrical point of view, interesting individuals both famous and unknown can be found in poses of all kinds. The costumes of the era can be inspected in their original glory and fashions spring to life, both on and off the stage, as performers posed not only 'in costume' but wearing their own 'street clothes'. The huge hats in many of the pictures in this book were a feature of every smart lady-about-town's outfit during the Edwardian period and up to the 1920s. What is particularly interesting is that in different copies of the same picture, the subject's clothes and hat – even hair or eyes sometimes – can be found tinted in different colours. When the time came for postcards to be hand-coloured, nobody was bothered about what colour the original had been: the touch-up artists often employed a good deal of artistic licence.

It was illegal until 1897 to 'deface' the side of the postcard on which the address was written by adding any kind of personal message, but throughout the early years of the 20th century, the scribbled comments and human detail which senders penned on the backs of their illustrated pictures add immense interest.

It became the fashion among theatregoers and fans of the great actors, players and performers of the day to collect theatrical postcards of their idols. Scenes from now hardly-remembered plays and shows, as well as long-forgotten stars of the music hall, circus and pantomime were immortalised and provide a fascinating glimpse into a by-gone era. Great names like Anna Pavlova, Ellen Terry, Henry Irving and Mrs. Patrick Campbell are of course among the ones easily recognised, but some of the great stars who were household names of the period have long since been forgotten. The pictures in this book pay an affectionate tribute to all of them. For just a glimpse of the diversity of what can be found on theatrical postcards is, to anyone with an interest in the history of the stage, like lifting the lid of a treasure chest. These pictures are the rare legacy of an earlier generation, links with those showmen and women known and unknown, the performers and their audiences who also recognised the magic of theatre – of whatever kind – gems to nurture and cherish.

The Stars – An Alphabetical Index

Ainley, Henry – Actor especially noted for Shakespearian and heroic roles. He was renowned for his good looks and reputedly possessed 'the most beautiful voice in the theatre'.

Allan, Maud – Exotic dancer who featured in a notorious court case.

Asche, Oscar – British actor who worked with Frank Benson and Beerbohm Tree, known for his Shakespearean roles. His greatest success was in his own musical fantasy Chu Chin Chow.

Barry, Shiel

Barrymore, Ethel - Trained with Sir Henry Irving and became the darling of turn-of-the-century society. She went to Broadway and became the First Lady of the American Theatre.

Bedells, Phyllis

Bourchier, Arthur

Brayton, Lily

Britton, Hutin

Brooke, Sarah

Burke, Billie

Campbell, Mrs Patrick – Famous English actress noted for her dramatic power and also her temperament. Corresponded with Shaw and notably created the role of Eliza Dolittle in his Pygmalion (1914).

Carlisle, Alexandra

Chase, Pauline - American actress of great beauty who became known in the London theatre for her portrayal of Peter Pan – she played the role in over 600 performances between 1906 and 1914.

Clifford, Camille

Collier, Constance

Courtneidge, Cecily

Coyne, Joseph

Creighton, Madge

140

Crawford, Alice
Cutler, Kate
Dare, Phyllis and Zena
Elsie, Lily
Evelyn, Clara
Fragson, Harry
Gill, Basil
Hoey, Iris
Irving, Ethel
Irving, Sir Henry – British actor-manager, famous for his Shakespearean roles
Lang, Matheson – Actor-manager who toured widely, appearing at various times with Lillie Langtree and Ellen Terry. Canadian-born, he toured Australia, South Africa and India with his own company, and in 1914, directed and acted in the first Shakespearean season at the Old Vic.
Lauzente, Raymond
Lohr, Marie
Loraine, Robert
Love, Mabel
Millar, Gertie
Millard, Evelyn
Minto, Dorothy
Neilson, Julia (see Fred Terry)
Neilson-Terry, Phyllis – Actress daughter of Fred Terry and Julia Neilson (see Fred Terry).
Passmore, Walter – Noted performer in Gilbert & Sullivan.
Pavlova, Anna – Famous ballerina who performed with the Diaghilev company and later toured the world with her own company. She was an inspiration to many who had never seen classical ballet, and acted as a hugely influential ambassadress for the dance.
Rae, Master Eric
Ray, Gabrielle
Soutar, Farren
Terry, Ellen (see Fred Terry)
Terry, Fred – Actor Manager Fred Terry (brother of the famous actress Ellen) and his wife and leading lady Julia Neilson might be described as the 'Kenneth Brannagh-Emma Thompson' or even the 'Posh and Becks' of their day. Their partnership on-stage lasted over thirty years, and they were recognised as the epitome of stardom and glamour.
Tree, Sir Herbert Beerbohm – Actor-manager whose larger-than-life personality both on the stage and off became identified with His Majesty's Theatre, where he was manager from 1897 – 1915. He also played a major role in the foundation of the Royal Academy of Dramatic Art in 1904.
Tree, Viola
Vanbrugh, Violet
Waller, Lewis – Glamorous actor-manager who specialised in romantic costume melodrama. He became the most successful matinee idol of the late 1800s and early 1900s. making such a hit with adoring female fans that they formed a group known as the KOWB (or the Keen On Waller Brigade).
Wehlem, Emmy